INTRODUCTION TO THE
THEORY OF FINITE GROUPS

UNIVERSITY MATHEMATICAL TEXTS

GENERAL EDITORS

ALEXANDER C. AITKEN, D.Sc., F.R.S.
DANIEL E. RUTHERFORD, Dr. Math.

Other volumes in preparation

INTRODUCTION TO THE
THEORY OF FINITE GROUPS

BY

WALTER LEDERMANN, Ph.D., D.Sc.

LECTURER IN MATHEMATICS IN THE UNIVERSITY OF MANCHESTER

OLIVER AND BOYD

EDINBURGH AND LONDON

NEW YORK : INTERSCIENCE PUBLISHERS, INC.

1949

FIRST PUBLISHED 1949

PRINTED IN GREAT BRITAIN BY
R. AND R. CLARK, LTD., EDINBURGH
FOR OLIVER AND BOYD, LTD., EDINBURGH

282929

PREFACE

ALTHOUGH the Theory of Groups occupies a position of fundamental importance in modern mathematics, it is still excluded from an Honours Course at a number of British Universities. This state of affairs is no doubt partly due to the fact that elementary expositions of the subject are not readily available in English, and it is hoped that this book will supply the remedy.

I have, therefore, endeavoured to make this introduction to the Theory of Groups of such an elementary character that it can be readily understood by an Honours student in his second or third year. With this end in view I have never hesitated to sacrifice completeness for breadth or to reject more modern methods when I considered alternative presentations to be more intelligible. Many will regret that the theory of matrix representation has not been included. In my opinion, however, this extensive subject should not be divorced from its context in the theory of linear associative algebras, and I felt that an adequate presentation of both of these disciplines was out of the question in the space at my disposal.

My warm thanks are due to the Editors for encouraging me to write this book, and especially to Dr. D. E. Rutherford for the great care and the helpful interest with which he has followed its progress from the day when the plan was first discussed during a holiday in the Highlands, until the last proof sheet was returned to the printers.

I am indebted to my colleague Mr. D. Rees for valuable suggestions and for checking the examples, and to my wife for helping with the proof reading and with the index.

v

Finally, I should like to express my appreciation of the efficiency with which the publishers have carried out their task under difficult conditions and of their never-failing courtesy.

W. LEDERMANN

MANCHESTER
May 1948

CONTENTS

CHAPTER IV

INVARIANT SUBGROUPS

CHAPTER V

SYLOW GROUPS AND PRIME POWER GROUPS

CHAPTER VI

ABELIAN GROUPS

CHAPTER I

THE GROUP CONCEPT

1. Introduction. The elementary operations of arithmetic consist in combining two numbers a and b in accordance with some well-defined rules so as to produce a unique third number c. For instance, if the **law of composition** be ordinary multiplication, we should have $c = ab$. When a and b are given, the number c can be found in each concrete case.

But we know that multiplication of two or more numbers obeys certain *formal laws* which hold for all products, irrespective of their numerical values, thus :

$$ab = ba \quad (commutative\ law) \qquad . \quad . \quad (1.1)$$
$$(ab)c = a(bc) \quad (associative\ law) \qquad . \quad . \quad (1.2)$$
$$1a = a1 = a. \quad . \qquad . \qquad . \quad . \quad . \quad (1.3)$$

The last equation serves to introduce one particular number called *unity*.

The second law states more explicitly that, if we put $ab = s$ and $bc = t$, then it is always true that $sc = at$.

In the axiomatic treatment of arithmetic it is customary to begin by laying down postulates or axioms such as (1.1), (1.2) and (1.3), and certain others dealing with addition as well as multiplication, and then to deduce the logical consequences of these postulates. It is immaterial, at the outset, whether the symbols a, b, . . . represent numbers as we normally understand them or other mathematical entities, or indeed whether they admit of any concrete interpretation at all. On the other hand, it will be conceded that it is the variety and depth of application in pure and applied mathe-

1

matics which has caused one conceivable system of axioms to be preferred to another.

2. The Axioms of Group Theory.   The abstract theory of groups deals with certain *sets of elements*

$$G : A, B, C, \ldots$$

with respect to which a *single law of composition* is defined. It is a matter of convention that the notation and nomenclature of *multiplication* are usually adopted to express the composition of abstract group elements.   Thus we assume that any two elements A, B of G, equal or unequal, possess a unique *product* C, and we write

$$AB = C.$$

It is the most typical property of a group that this product C is itself one of its elements or, as it is often expressed, that a group is *closed with respect to multiplication*.

A complete system of axioms which a set G must obey, if it is to be a group, is given in the following:

DEFINITION 1.   *A set G of a finite or infinite number of elements, for which a law of composition ("multiplication") is defined, forms a group if the following conditions are satisfied:*

(I) **Closure :**   *to every ordered* * *pair of elements* A, B *of* G *there belongs a unique element* C *of* G, *written*

$$C = AB,$$

which is called the product of A *and* B.

(II) **Associative law :**   *if* A, B, C *are any three elements of* G, *which need not be distinct, then*

$$(AB)C = A(BC),$$

so that either side may be denoted by ABC.

* I.e. the pairs A, B and B, A are regarded as distinct if $A \neq B$.

(III) **Unit element :** G *contains an* * *element* I, *called the unit element or* **identity** *such that for every element* A *of* G

$$AI = IA = A.$$

(IV) **Inverse** or **reciprocal element :** *corresponding to every element* A *of* G, *there exists in* G *an* * *element* A^{-1} *such that*

$$AA^{-1} = A^{-1}A = I.$$

It will be observed that these postulates closely resemble those which govern ordinary multiplication, except that the *commutative law* is not required to hold for groups.

DEFINITION 2. *A group which has the* additional *property that for every two of its elements*

$$AB = BA$$

is called an **Abelian** † (*or* **commutative**) *group.*

The waiving of the commutative law for groups in general makes it necessary to distinguish between the elements AB and BA, which are sometimes called the right- or left-hand products of A by B.

It is quite possible that while the commutative law does not hold throughout the group, it may yet be valid for certain individual pairs of elements.

DEFINITION 3. *Two elements* A, B *are said to commute* (*or to be* **commutative,** *or* **permutable**) *if*

$$AB = BA.$$

It is worth while to dwell a little longer on the significance and immediate consequences of the group axioms stated in Definition 1, p. 2.

The *associative law* was enunciated only for three elements, but can in fact be easily proved in its more

---

* Its uniqueness will be proved later on, see pp. 5 and 6.
† After N. H. Abel (1802–29).

general form, namely that, without ambiguity,

$$(A_1 A_2 \ldots A_r)(A_{r+1}, \ldots A_n)$$
$$= (A_1 A_2 \ldots A_s)(A_{s+1} \ldots A_n), \quad (1.4)$$

where r and s are any two integers between 1 and n. Since when $n = 3$, (1.4) is equivalent to axiom (II), we have a basis of mathematical induction with respect to n, the number of factors. There is no loss of generality in assuming that $s < r < n$. Hence, by induction,

$$A_1 A_2 \ldots A_r = (A_1 A_2 \ldots A_s)(A_{s+1} \ldots A_r),$$

and the left-hand side of (1.4) becomes

$$[(A_1 \ldots A_s)(A_{s+1} \ldots A_r)](A_{r+1} \ldots A_n) = [B_1 B_2] B_3,$$

where the products in round brackets have been denoted by B_1, B_2, B_3 respectively. Again, the right-hand side may be expressed as

$$(A_1 \ldots A_s)[(A_{s+1} \ldots A_r)(A_{r+1} \ldots A_n)] = B_1[B_2 B_3].$$

In virtue of axiom (II)

$$[B_1 B_2] B_3 = B_1[B_2 B_3],$$

which proves the proposition (1.4). We are therefore entitled to omit the brackets altogether and denote either side of (1.4) by

$$A_1 A_2 \ldots A_n.$$

In particular, when all factors are identical we shall, as in ordinary algebra, write

$$AA \qquad\qquad = A^2,$$
$$(AA)A = A(AA) = A^3,$$
$$\ldots\ldots\ldots\ldots\ldots\ldots\ldots\ldots$$

Also, when n and m are positive integers,

$$A^m A^n = A^n A^m = A^{m+n} \quad . \quad . \quad . \quad (1.5)$$

and

$$(A^m)^n = A^{mn}. \quad . \quad . \quad . \quad . \quad (1.6)$$

It is interesting to note that the familiar law of indices and the manipulation of powers of a *single* quantity finds its ultimate justification in the associative law of multiplication.

When A and B are distinct elements, we have in general

$$(AB)^n \neq A^n B^n \;;$$

but when A and B commute,

$$(AB)^n = ABAB \ldots AB = A^n B^n \quad . \quad . \quad (1.7)$$

and

$$A^m B^n = B^n A^m,$$

since we may rearrange the order of the factors as we please.

Multiplication by the **unit element** I, whether used as a right or a left factor, leaves every element of G unaltered. It follows that there can be only *one* such element. For supposing that J had the same properties as I, let us consider the product

$$IJ.$$

Since premultiplication by I leaves J unaltered, we have $IJ = J$; on the other hand, as postmultiplication by J has no effect on I, it follows that $IJ = I$; hence

$$J = IJ = I,$$

which proves the uniqueness of the unit element.

Also,

$$I = I^2 = I^3 = \ldots = I^n. \quad . \quad . \quad (1.8)$$

The existence, within the group, of an *inverse* for every element A means that not only multiplication, but also left and right " division ", can be carried out within a group. Thus if A and B be any elements whatsoever, there exist elements X and Y such that

$$AX = B, \quad YA = B. \quad . \quad . \quad (1.9)$$

In fact we can express the solutions in the form

$$X = A^{-1}B, \quad Y = BA^{-1},$$

using the element A^{-1} referred to in postulate (IV) on p. 3. This argument also proves that the solutions of (1.9) are unique ; for if

$$AX_1 = AX_2 = B,$$

it would follow that

$$A^{-1}(AX_1) = A^{-1}(AX_2),$$

and therefore

$$X_1 = X_2.$$

Again, since A^{-1} itself is a solution of these equations when $B = I$, we infer that the inverse of any given element is *unique*.

It is important to note that A commutes with A^{-1}. Hence by (1.8) and (1.7)

$$I = I^n = (AA^{-1})^n = A^n(A^{-1})^n,$$

so that $(A^{-1})^n$ is the inverse of A^n ; it is customary to write

$$(A^n)^{-1} = (A^{-1})^n = A^{-n}. \qquad . \qquad . \qquad (1.10)$$

The reader will have no difficulty in convincing himself that the rules (1.5) and (1.6) are still valid when m or n are negative integers or zero, provided we put

$$A^0 = I. \qquad . \qquad . \qquad . \qquad (1.11)$$

In particular we observe that two powers of the same element always commute, thus

$$A^k A^l = A^l A^k. \qquad . \qquad . \qquad (1.12)$$

Since, for any two elements A and B,

$$(AB)(B^{-1}A^{-1}) = ABB^{-1}A^{-1} = I,$$

we have

$$(AB)^{-1} = B^{-1}A^{-1},$$

and more generally,

$$(AB \ldots K)^{-1} = K^{-1} \ldots B^{-1}A^{-1}. \qquad . \qquad (1.13)$$

Lastly, we remark that I is the only **idempotent** element of the group, i.e. the only solution of the equation

$$X^2 = X. \qquad . \qquad . \qquad . \qquad . \qquad (1.14)$$

For on multiplying (1.14) by X^{-1} we obtain

$$X^{-1}X^2 = X^{-1}X,$$

i.e. $X = I.$

3. Examples of Infinite Groups. The groups we are going to mention in this section contain an infinity of elements and are therefore called **infinite groups**.

(i) *All positive rational numbers form a group with respect to ordinary multiplication.* Indeed the product of two rational numbers is a rational number, the unit element is the rational number 1, and the inverse of every positive rational number is also such a number. This group is Abelian.

By way of contrast we might point out that the set of *positive integers* does *not* form a group with respect to multiplication, because the fourth postulate, the existence of an inverse, is not fulfilled.

(ii) *The set of all integers forms an Abelian group with respect to addition.* In this case it is customary to express the composition of elements by such an equation as

$$a + b = c.$$

The unit element is the number 0, because

$$a + 0 = 0 + a = a,$$

and the inverse of a is $-a$.

(iii) *Rotations about a fixed point*: if a rigid body is free to move about a fixed point O, every displacement of the body is equivalent to a rotation through an angle α about a line l passing through O. Such a displacement will be denoted by (l, α), or more briefly by a single letter A. If B is another displacement of the same kind, the product

AB is defined as the displacement which results when A and B are carried out in succession (in this order *). This being the law of composition it is easy to verify the group postulates. The unit element is the " displacement " which, in fact, leaves the body in its original position, i.e. $I = (l, 0)$, where l is arbitrary. The inverse of (l, α) is $(l, -\alpha)$. We shall later (p. 87) prove the associative law for a certain general class of operations which includes the present type of displacement. The following illustration demonstrates that the commutative law is not always fulfilled : let 1234

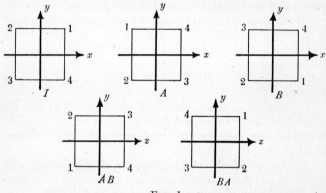

Fig. 1

denote a square lamina initially placed in the (x, y)-plane as indicated in fig. 1, the axis of z being at right angles to the plane of the lamina. We assume that $Oxyz$ is a right-handed system of reference, which is fixed in space. If, in the above notation,

$$A = \left(z, \frac{\pi}{4}\right), \quad B = (x, \pi),$$

it is easily verified that AB and BA give rise to different positions of the lamina so that $AB \neq BA$.

* Some authors take the reverse order.

(iv) *Groups of matrices* : the reader who is familiar with the elementary properties of matrices * will appreciate the excellent illustration of group theory afforded by matrix algebra and in particular by matrix multiplication. For the discussion of the associative law, the existence of the unit matrix and the reciprocal matrix, see *op. cit.* p. 12 and p. 53 respectively, or Chapter III, § 27 of the present book.

The following sets of matrices form groups with respect to matrix multiplication :

(a) *all non-singular matrices of a fixed order* n,
(b) *all orthogonal matrices of a fixed order* n,
(c) *all orthogonal matrices of a fixed order and of determinant* $+1$.

4. Alternative Axioms for Finite Groups. Groups which consist of a finite number of elements are of especial interest, and we shall henceforth be concerned only with **finite groups** unless the contrary is expressly stated. The number of elements in a finite group is called the **order** of the group.

In the case of finite groups the fundamental axioms (p. 2) may be replaced by the following alternative system of postulates which are sometimes easier to verify :

THEOREM 1. *A finite set of elements, for which a law of composition ("multiplication") is defined, forms a group if*

(a) *the set is closed with respect to multiplication* ;
(b) *the associative law is satisfied*;
(c) *right and left cancelling is permitted, i.e. each of the equations*
$$AX = BX \quad \text{and} \quad YA = YB$$

implies that $A = B$.

Proof. We shall show that condition (c) entails axioms (III) and (IV) on p. 3, i.e. we shall *deduce* from (c) the

* See A. C. Aitken, *Determinants and Matrices*, 4th edition.

B

existence of the unit and inverse elements.   Let

$$A_1, A_2, \ldots, A_g \quad . \quad . \quad . \quad (1.15)$$

be the g distinct elements of the group G. If A be any one of them, the products

$$AA_1, AA_2, \ldots, AA_g \quad . \quad . \quad . \quad (1.16)$$

are elements of G in virtue of (a) and are distinct, because, by (c), an equation of the form $AA_i = AA_j$ implies that $A_i = A_j$. Thus the g elements written down in (1.16) are merely a different arrangement of those in (1.15). Therefore if X be any element of G whatsoever, there exists an element A_u such that

$$AA_u = X, \quad . \quad . \quad . \quad (1.17)$$

because X, which occurs in (1.15), must have a counterpart in (1.16).

Similarly, on postmultiplying the set (1.15) by A we conclude that there exists an element A_u such that

$$A_v A = X. \quad . \quad . \quad . \quad (1.18)$$

These conclusions apply in particular to the case when $A = X$, i.e. we infer that G contains two elements A_0 and A_0' such that

$$AA_0 = A \quad . \quad . \quad . \quad (1.19)$$

and

$$A_0'A = A. \quad . \quad . \quad . \quad (1.20)$$

On premultiplying (1.17) by A_0' we obtain $A_0'X = A_0'(AA_u) = (A_0'A)A_u = AA_u = X$,

i.e. $$A_0'X = X. \quad . \quad . \quad . \quad (1.21)$$

Similarly,

$$XA_0 = X. \quad . \quad . \quad . \quad (1.22)$$

Thus we have shown that in equations (1.19) and (1.20) A may be replaced by X which, it will be remembered, was an arbitrary element of G, i.e. any element whatsoever remains unaltered when premultiplied by A_0' or postmultiplied by A_0'. In particular, on putting X equal to A_0 in (1.21) and X equal to A_0' in (1.22), we find that

$$A_0 = A_0' A_0 = A_0'.$$

This establishes the existence of a *unit element*, namely

$$I = A_0 = A_0' ;$$

its uniqueness follows at once by an application of (c) to the equation $AI = A$.

Let us now return to equations (1.17) and (1.18) and consider the case in which $X = I$. We conclude that G contains two elements A_r and A_r' such that

$$A A_r = I$$

and

$$A_r' A = I.$$

In order to prove that these two elements are equal we simplify the product $A_r' A A_r$ in two different ways by appealing to the associative law, namely

$$A_r' A A_r = (A_r' A) A_r = I A_r = A_r$$

and

$$A_r' A A_r = A_r' (A A_r) = A_r' I = A_r',$$

whence

$$A_r = A_r' = A^{-1},$$

say. The uniqueness of A^{-1} follows from the fact that, according to (c), there cannot be more than one solution of the equation

$$A X = I.$$

5. The Multiplication Table. In the abstract theory of groups when no reference is made to the nature of the elements, the group must be considered completely specified if all possible products AB are known or can be determined. For a finite group of order g there are g^2 such products, which may conveniently be listed in a $g \times g$ **multiplication table** as was suggested by A. Cayley.[*]

---

[*] *Phil. Mag.* vol. vii (**4**), 1854.

Example. We shall give a detailed discussion of a group of order 6 which may in many ways be regarded as typical. The elements will be denoted by

$$I, A, B, C, D, E, \qquad . \qquad . \qquad . \quad (1.23)$$

and the 36 products formed by them are set out in the following table :

	I	A	B	C	D	E
I	I	A	B	C	D	E
A	A	B	I	E	C	D
B	B	I	A	D	E	C
C	C	D	E	I	A	B
D	D	E	C	B	I	A
E	E	C	D	A	B	I

Table 1

For example, the product CD is that element which stands at the intersection of the row marked C and the column marked D ; thus $CD = A$. Similarly, we find that $BA = I$, $EB = D$ and so on. Our task is to verify that the rules for composition summarized in Table 1 do in fact obey the group axioms laid down in Theorem 1 on p. 14 : the system (1.23) is obviously *closed* (postulate (a)) because the product of any two elements is again one of the six elements of the set. The *cancelling rule* (c) is also fulfilled ; for if U and V be distinct elements of the set, then $XU \neq XV$ whatever element X may be chosen ; this is seen at once from the table where the various elements XU occupy the row marked X, and inspection shows that the elements in each row are distinct. The direct verification of the *associative law* (b) would be rather laborious as all possible equations of the form

$$(XY)Z = X(YZ) \qquad . \qquad . \qquad . \quad (1.24)$$

would have to be examined ; however, we shall later learn how this difficulty can often be overcome by indirect

methods, and we shall then return to this example (p. 70).
In the meantime the reader is recommended to check
equation (1.24) at least in some particular cases, e.g.

$$(AC)D = ED = B,$$
$$A(CD) = AA = B.$$

Table 1 is not symmetrical with respect to the main
diagonal, which illustrates the fact that in general
$XY \neq YX$. But it will be observed that the element I
always lies either on the diagonal or else occupies positions
which are symmetrically placed in pairs about the diagonal.
This illustrates the property that every element commutes
with its inverse, e.g. $AB = BA = I$, showing that A and B
are inverse elements of each other.

The rows and columns, including their headings, may
be rearranged amongst themselves without affecting the
information contained in the multiplication table. It is
sometimes convenient to specify the rows not by the
elements themselves but by their inverses ; thus Table 1
is equivalent to

	I	A	B	C	D	E
I	I	A	B	C	D	E
A^{-1}	B	I	A	D	E	C
B^{-1}	A	B	I	E	C	D
C^{-1}	C	D	E	I	A	B
D^{-1}	D	E	C	B	I	A
E^{-1}	E	C	D	A	B	I

Table 2

In a multiplication table of this type the unit element
naturally occupies all the positions of the main diagonal.

Postulate (c) on p. 9 is equivalent to the demand that
no element be repeated in any one row or column of the
$g \times g$ multiplication table, i.e. all g elements appear in
some order in each row or column. Such an arrangement
is commonly called a *latin square*. But it is not true that

conversely every latin square can be interpreted as the multiplication table of a finite group ; for while the condition of closure and cancelling would indeed be fulfilled, the associative law might not be satisfied. This is shown by the following example ($g = 5$).   In the latin square

	I	A	B	C	D
I	I	A	B	C	D
A	A	I	D	B	C
B	B	C	I	D	A
C	C	D	A	I	B
D	D	B	C	A	I

Table 3

the break-down of the associative law is exemplified by the equations

$$(AB)C = DC = A,$$
$$A(BC) = AD = C.$$

Thus Table 3 cannot be regarded as the multiplication table of a group.

6. Examples of Finite Groups.

(i) *The numbers* 1, i, -1, $-$i *form an Abelian group of order* 4 *with respect to ordinary multiplication* ($i = \sqrt{-1}$). The reader is recommended to construct the 4×4 multiplication table.

(ii) Consider the six functions

$$f_1(z) = z, \quad f_2(z) = \frac{1}{1-z}, \quad f_3(z) = \frac{z-1}{z},$$

$$f_4(z) = \frac{1}{z}, \quad f_5(z) = 1-z, \quad f_6(z) = \frac{z}{z-1},$$

which are the values of the cross-ratio of four points when these points are permuted in all possible ways, and let the law of composition be defined as *substitution of one function in another* ; e.g.

$$f_4 f_3 = f_4\{f_3(z)\} = \frac{1}{f_3(z)} = \frac{z}{z-1} = f_6,$$

and so on. It will be found that these functions form a *closed* set, the part of the *unit element* being played by $f_1(z)$. The multiplication table is readily constructed thus :

	f_1	f_2	f_3	f_4	f_5	f_6
f_1	f_1	f_2	f_3	f_4	f_5	f_6
f_2	f_2	f_3	f_1	f_6	f_4	f_5
f_3	f_3	f_1	f_2	f_5	f_6	f_4
f_4	f_4	f_5	f_6	f_1	f_2	f_3
f_5	f_5	f_6	f_4	f_3	f_1	f_2
f_6	f_6	f_4	f_5	f_2	f_3	f_1

Table 4

The *associative law* can be verified or established by indirect arguments (Chap. III, § 27).

(iii) *Classes of residues.* Every positive integer (>1) gives rise to a certain finite Abelian group in the following way : let m be a fixed positive integer (>1), which will henceforth be referred to as the **modulus**. *Two integers* x *and* y *are said to be* **congruent** *to each other with regard to the modulus* m *if* m *is a factor of* x $-$ y ; *we write symbolically*

$$x \equiv y \pmod{m}.$$

Thus two integers are congruent with respect to m if and only if they differ by an exact (positive or negative) multiple of m ; e.g. $3 \equiv 18 \pmod{5}$, $-2 \equiv 14 \pmod{8}$, $12 \equiv 0 \pmod{3}$.

It follows that any integer whatsoever is congruent, with regard to the modulus m, to one and only one of the numbers

$$0, 1, 2, \ldots, m-2, m-1, \qquad . \qquad . \quad (1.25)$$

which are therefore said to form a **complete set of residues** relative to m ; they are in fact the least non-negative residues relative to m.

Bearing in mind that the congruence relation

$$x \equiv y \ (\text{mod. } m)$$

is equivalent to an equation of the form

$$x = y + km$$

where k is a certain integer, it is easy to verify the following rules : *if* $x_1 \equiv y_1$ (mod. m) *and* $x_2 \equiv y_2$ (mod. m), *then*

(A) $$c_1 x_1 + c_2 x_2 \equiv c_1 y_1 + c_2 y_2 \ (\text{mod. } m),$$

where c_1 *and* c_2 *are any integers, and*

(M) $$x_1 x_2 \equiv y_1 y_2 \ (\text{mod. } m).$$

These rules show a remarkable resemblance to those for ordinary equations. Yet the following important difference should be carefully noted : while the equation $kx = ky$ implies that $x = y$ provided $k \neq 0$, we can only state that

(D) $$kx \equiv ky \ (\text{mod. } m) \qquad . \qquad . \qquad . \ (1.26)$$

implies that

$$x \equiv y \ (\text{mod. } m), \textit{ provided} * \ (m, k) = 1.$$

Indeed (1.26) is equivalent to the statement,†

$$m \mid k(x - y),$$

and if m is prime to k, it follows that

$$m \mid x - y,$$

i.e. $$x \equiv y \ (\text{mod. } m).$$

The number of integers between 0 *and* m *which are prime to* m *is denoted by* $\phi(m)$ (**Euler's function**). Thus, $\phi(9)$ denotes the number of integers between 0 and 8 which are

---

* We use the symbol (a, b) to denote the highest common factor of a and b ; in particular $(m, k) = 1$ means that m and k are (relatively) prime.

† The symbol $a \mid b$ expresses that a is a factor of b, i.e. that there exists an integer q such that $b = aq$. We shall use the fact that if $a \mid bc$ and $(a, c) = 1$, then $a \mid b$.

prime to 9 ; there are evidently six such integers, namely 1, 2, 4, 5, 7, 8 and so $\phi(9) = 6$.

If p be a prime number, all but the first of the integers 0, 1, 2, ..., $p-1$ are prime to p, whence

$$\phi(p) = p - 1. \qquad . \qquad . \qquad . \qquad . \qquad (1.27)$$

Again, if $m = p^r$, only the multiples of p in the set 0, 1, 2, ..., $p^r - 1$ are not prime to p^r ; as there are evidently p^{r-1} such multiples, namely hp where $h = 0, 1, 2, ..., p^{r-1} - 1$, it follows that

$$\phi(p^r) = p^r - p^{r-1}. \qquad . \qquad . \qquad . \qquad (1.28)$$

It is customary to put

$$\phi(1) = 1. \qquad . \qquad . \qquad . \qquad . \qquad (1.29)$$

Those of the numbers (1.25) which are prime to m form a sub-set M which we shall denote by

$$M: a_1, a_2, ..., a_{\phi(m)}, \qquad . \qquad . \qquad . \qquad (1.30)$$

where $0 < a_i < m$. One of these numbers, say a_1, is equal to 1. The product of any two is a number which is certainly prime to m though it may be greater than m and therefore not included in (1.30) ; but it is in any case *congruent* to one of these residues, as is indeed any integer which is prime to m. Thus we may write

$$a_i a_k \equiv a_l \ (\text{mod. } m) \qquad . \qquad . \qquad . \qquad (1.31)$$

and define a law of composition for residues as *ordinary multiplication followed* (if necessary) *by reduction to the least positive residue with regard to* m ; e.g.

$$4 \times 5 \equiv 2 \ (\text{mod. } 9), \quad 2 \times 7 \equiv 5 \ (\text{mod. } 9) \ etc.$$

It is clear that this law of composition, being derived from ordinary multiplication, is both *commutative* and *associative*. Again, as we are concerned only with residues prime to m, Rule (D) (p. 16) may be applied, i.e. if a, b and x be any members of M, then

$$ax \equiv bx' \ (\text{mod. } m) \ implies \ that \ a \equiv b \ (\text{mod. } m).$$

This establishes the *cancelling rule* (c) of Theorem 1, p. 9. Thus we can summarize our results in the

THEOREM 2. *The least positive residues prime to* m *form an Abelian group* M *of order* $\phi(m)$ *if the law of composition be defined as multiplication followed by reduction relative to the modulus* m.

The unit element of M is obviously equal to 1, which always occurs in the set (1.30). Also since M is a group, every element a of M possesses a unique inverse a' such that

$$aa' \equiv 1 \ (\text{mod. } m),$$

or expressed as an ordinary equation

$$aa' = 1 + xm, \quad . \quad . \quad . \quad . \quad (1.32)$$

where x is a certain integer. If b be any number prime to m, it is of the form

$$b = a + ym, \quad . \quad . \quad . \quad (1.33)$$

where a is a suitable element of M. On multiplying (1.33) by a' and substituting for aa' from (1.32) we get

$$a'b - (a'y + x)m = 1.$$

This is a well-known result,* namely that *if* b *and* m *are relatively prime, then integers* u *and* v *exist such that*

$$ub + vm = 1 ; \quad . \quad . \quad . \quad (1.34)$$

in our notation $u = a'$ and $v = a'y + x$.

7. Isomorphic Groups. On closer scrutiny it will be observed that Table 1 (p. 12) differs from Table 4 (p. 15) merely in respect of notation, so that from an abstract point of view they are regarded as representing the same group. In fact, if we establish the (1, 1)-correspondence

---

* The argument in the text is not offered as a proof of (1.34), which is usually obtained by means of Euclid's algorithm, and in its turn forms the basis of rule D.

$$f_1 \longleftrightarrow I, \quad f_2 \longleftrightarrow A, \quad f_3 \longleftrightarrow B,$$
$$f_4 \longleftrightarrow C, \quad f_5 \longleftrightarrow D, \quad f_6 \longleftrightarrow E \qquad . \qquad . \quad (1.35)$$

the identity of the tables becomes evident ; i.e. any relation derived from Table 4 is in virtue of the correspondence (1.35) carried over into a correct relation between the elements of Table 1, and vice versa; e.g.

$$f_4 f_3 = f_6 \quad \text{becomes} \quad CB = E.$$

This is an illustration of a concept which is of fundamental importance in the theory of groups.

DEFINITION 4. *Two groups* $G = \{A, B, \ldots\}$ *and* $G' = \{A', B', \ldots\}$ *are said to be* **isomorphic** * *if a* (1, 1)-*correspondence*

$$A \longleftrightarrow A', \quad B \longleftrightarrow B', \ldots$$

can be established between their elements such that

$$AB = C \quad implies \quad A'B' = C',$$

and vice versa, or more briefly if

$$(AB)' = A'B'.$$

Paraphrasing this definition we may say that *isomorphic groups have the same* **structure** *although they may differ in respect of the notation and nature of their elements.*

Example 1. The following groups of order 4 are isomorphic, the law of composition for each being stated in brackets :

(α) *the numbers* $1, i, -1, -i,$ \qquad (*ordinary multiplication*)

(β) *the matrices* \hfill (*matrix multiplication*)

$$\begin{bmatrix} 1 & 0 \\ 0 & 1 \end{bmatrix}, \quad \begin{bmatrix} 0 & 1 \\ -1 & 0 \end{bmatrix}, \quad \begin{bmatrix} -1 & 0 \\ 0 & -1 \end{bmatrix}, \quad \begin{bmatrix} 0 & -1 \\ 1 & 0 \end{bmatrix}$$

(γ) *the residues* $1, 2, 3, 4$ (mod. 5) \qquad (*multiplication and reduction* mod. 5)

---

* Some authors use the expression " *simply isomorphic* " in this connection, see footnote on p. 106.

Indeed if the elements of each set be renamed I, A, B, C (in this order), their common multiplication table is seen to be

	I	A	B	C
I	I	A	B	C
A	A	B	C	I
B	B	C	I	A
C	C	I	A	B

Table 5

E.g. the abstract equation

$$CB = A$$

is interpreted

in (α) as $(-i)(-1) = i$,

in (β) as $\begin{bmatrix} 0 & -1 \\ 1 & 0 \end{bmatrix} \begin{bmatrix} -1 & 0 \\ 0 & -1 \end{bmatrix} = \begin{bmatrix} 0 & 1 \\ -1 & 0 \end{bmatrix}$

in (γ) as $4 \times 3 \equiv 2$ (mod. 5).

In a similar manner all other properties of the abstract Table 5 are reflected in the concrete groups (α), (β) and (γ).

Example 2. Consider the following groups of order 4 where in each case the law of composition is stated in brackets :

(a) *the functions* z, $-z$, $\dfrac{1}{z}$, $-\dfrac{1}{z}$ (*substitution*, see p. 14)

(b) *the matrices* (*matrix multiplication*)

$\begin{bmatrix} 1 & 0 \\ 0 & 1 \end{bmatrix}$, $\begin{bmatrix} 1 & 0 \\ 0 & -1 \end{bmatrix}$, $\begin{bmatrix} -1 & 0 \\ 0 & 1 \end{bmatrix}$, $\begin{bmatrix} -1 & 0 \\ 0 & -1 \end{bmatrix}$

(c) *the residues* 1, 3, 5, 7 (mod. 8)   (*multiplication and reduction* mod. 8)

If the elements of each set be denoted by I, A, B, C, it will be seen that they have the same multiplication table, namely

	I	A	B	C
I	I	A	B	C
A	A	I	C	B
B	B	C	I	A
C	C	B	A	I

Table 6

It is left to the reader to verify this statement. We would point out, however, that the groups represented by Tables 5 and 6 respectively are certainly *not* isomorphic ; in the latter the square of each element is equal to I, which is evidently not the case in Table 5. Incidentally, we have learned that groups of the same order may well be of different structure.

8. The Order (Period) of an Element. Let A be an element of a group G of order g and consider the set of powers of A,

$$I, A, A^2, A^3, \ldots, \qquad \cdot \quad \cdot \quad \cdot \quad (1.36)$$

all of which are of course elements of G. Since G is a finite group, these elements cannot all be distinct, i.e. we must have a relation

$$A^k = A^l,$$

where $k > l$, say. Hence

$$A^{k-l} = I,$$

which shows that in a finite group some power of every element is equal to the unit element.

DEFINITION 5. *The least positive power of* A *which is equal to the unit element is called the* **order** (*or* **period**) *of* A.

Thus if A is of order h, then

$$A^h = I,$$

but

$$A^x \neq I,$$

when $0 < x < h$.

Again, if m be a multiple of h, say

$$m = hq,$$

we have

$$A^m = (A^h)^q = I^q = I.$$

The converse of this proposition is also true ; in fact, we shall prove

THEOREM 3.   *If A is of order* h, *then* $A^m = I$ *if, and only if,* m *is a multiple of* h.

Proof.   Divide m by h and let q be the quotient and r the remainder, thus

$$m = hq + r,$$

where

$$0 \leqslant r < h. \qquad . \qquad . \qquad . \qquad . \quad (1.37)$$

Hence

$$I = A^m = A^{hq+r} = A^{hq}A^r = I^q A^r = A^r.$$

Since h is the order of A, this equation is impossible unless $r = 0$; i.e. m must be a multiple of h.

The following facts about the order of an element are frequently used :

(i) *The unit element* I *is the only element of order one.*

(ii) *The elements* A *and* A^{-1} *are always of the same order* (see (iv)).

(iii) *If* $B = P^{-1}AP$ *where* P *is any element whatsoever, then* A *and* B *are of the same order.*   For

$$B^2 = (P^{-1}AP)(P^{-1}AP) = P^{-1}AIAP = P^{-1}A^2P,$$

and generally,

$$B^k = P^{-1}A^kP, \quad A^k = PB^kP^{-1} ;$$

thus if $A^k = I$, we have $B^k = P^{-1}IP = I$, and vice versa.

(iv) *The order of any power of* A *cannot exceed the order of* A.   For if $A^h = I$ and $B = A^s$, then $B^h = A^{sh} = (A^h)^s = I^s = I$. Moreover, *if* A *be of order* h *and if* s *be prime to* h, *then* A^s *and* A *are of the same order.*   As $(s, h) = 1$, we can find two integers u and v (see p. 18) such that $us + vh = 1$. Hence if $B = A^s$, we have

$$B^u = A^{us} = A^{1-vh} = AA^{-vh} = AI = A.$$

Therefore, A is a power of B which is itself a power of A, whence A and B are of the same order.

The following theorem allows us to resolve a given element of composite order into factors of simpler orders:

THEOREM 4. *If C be of order* mn *where* m *and* n *are relatively prime, then* C *can be expressed in one, and only one, way as the product of two commutative elements* A *and* B *of orders* m *and* n *respectively.*

Proof. 1. Let $A = C^n$ and $B = C^m$; the elements A and B commute because they are powers of the same element C. We have

$$A^m = C^{nm} = I, \quad B^n = C^{mn} = I,$$

whence we infer that m and n are the orders of A and B respectively; for if a smaller (positive) power of A or B were equal to the unit element, we should get a contradiction to the fact that C was of order mn.

Since m and n are relatively prime, we can find integers u and v (see (1.34)) such that

$$un + vm = 1. \quad . \quad . \quad . \quad . \quad (1.38)$$

Hence

$$C = C^{un+vm} = (C^n)^u (C^m)^v = A^u B^v.$$

We deduce from (1.38) that u is prime to m; for if any factor (> 1) were common to u and m, it would divide each term on the left-hand side of (1.38) and therefore also the right-hand side, which is absurd. Hence by proposition (iv), p. 22, A^u is of order m. Similarly, B^v is of order n. Also, since A and B commute, so do A^u and B^v. Thus if we put

$$M = A^u, \quad N = B^v$$

we have

$$C = MN, \quad . \quad . \quad . \quad . \quad (1.39)$$

where M and N fulfil all the conditions of the theorem.

2. In order to prove the uniqueness of the decomposition (1.39) suppose that

$$C = MN = M_1 N_1, \quad . \quad . \quad . \quad (1.40)$$

where M commutes with N, and M_1 with N_1, and where the orders of M and M_1 are m, and those of N and N_1 are n. Raising (1.40) to the (nu)th power, we get

$$M^{nu}N^{nu} = M_1{}^{nu}N_1{}^{nu},$$
$$M^{nu} = M_1{}^{nu},$$

whence by using (1.38)

$$M^{1-mv} = M_1{}^{1-mv},$$
$$M(M^m)^{-v} = M_1(M_1{}^m)^{-v},$$
$$MI^{-v} = M_1I^{-v},$$

i.e.

$$M = M_1.$$

Equation (1.40) now at once shows that, likewise,

$$N = N_1.$$

9. Cyclic Groups.

DEFINITION 6. *A group whose elements can all be expressed as powers of a single element is called a* **cyclic group**.

The general form of a cyclic group of order c is

$$C : I, A, A^2, \ldots, A^{c-1}, \qquad . \qquad . \quad (1.41)$$

where c is the least positive integer such that

$$A^c = I.$$

We say that C is **generated** by A.

The order of a cyclic group is equal to that of its generating element ; conversely, *if a group of order* c *contain an element of order* c, *then the group is cyclic*. The generating element is not uniquely determined ; indeed if e be any integer prime to c and $0 < e < c$, then A^e may be taken as the generating element of the group (1.41) (see (iv) p. 22).

All cyclic groups of the same order are isomorphic, as

may be seen by making their generating elements correspond to one another; *there is, in fact, one, and only one (abstract), cyclic group for any given order.*

All cyclic groups are Abelian.

Example 1. If $\gamma = e^{2\pi i/c}$ (a primitive c^{th} root of unity), then the numbers

$$1, \gamma, \gamma^2, \ldots, \gamma^{c-1}$$

form a cyclic group of order c with respect to multiplication, because c is the least positive exponent such that $\gamma^c = 1$.

Example 2. The residues

$$0, 1, 2, \ldots, m-1$$

with respect to the modulus m form a cyclic group of order m, if the law of composition be addition followed by reduction to the least non-negative residue relative to m; e.g., if $m > 4$

$$(m-2) + 4 = m + 2 \equiv 2,$$
$$(m-3) + 3 = m \quad \equiv 0.$$

The operations $I, A, A^2, \ldots, A^{c-1}$ of a cyclic group may be interpreted geometrically as rotations in a plane about a fixed point O. The group is generated by the rotation through an angle $2\pi/c$; any point on which this operation is carried out c times in succession, just describes a complete circle (hence the name " cyclic " group).

Examples

(1) Prove that the following sets of numbers form infinite (Abelian) groups with respect to ordinary multiplication :

(a) $\{2^k\}$ $(k = 0, \pm 1, \pm 2, \ldots)$.

(b) $\left\{ \dfrac{1 + 2m}{1 + 2n} \right\}$ $(m, n = 0, \pm 1, \pm 2, \ldots)$.

(c) $\{\cos \theta + i \sin \theta\}$, where θ is a rational number.

(2) Why do the positive rational numbers not form a group when the law of composition for a and b be defined as a/b ?

(3) If A be the operation which replaces x by $\alpha x + \beta$, prove

C

that A is of finite order if, and only if, α is a root of unity other than 1.

In examples (4) to (8) the associative law is assumed to hold for all elements involved.

(4) If A, B and AB are of order 2, prove that A and B commute.

(5) Prove that the elements AB and BA have the same order.

(6) If $BA = A^m B^n$, prove that the elements $A^m B^{n-2}$, $A^{m-2} B^n$ and AB^{-1} have the same order.

(7) If $B^{-1}AB = A^k$, prove that $B^{-r} A^s B^r = A^{sk^r}$.

(8) If $AB = BA^k$, show that $A^u B^v = B^v A^{uk^v}$ and $(B^v A^u)^t = B^{tv} A^w$, where $w = u(k^{tv} - 1)/(k^v - 1)$.

(9) Prove that a group is Abelian if, and only if, the correspondence $A \longleftrightarrow A^{-1}$, $B \longleftrightarrow B^{-1}$, ... represents an isomorphism.

(10) Show that a group of even order contains an odd number of elements of order 2.

(11) Show that the matrices

$$\begin{bmatrix} 1 & 0 \\ 0 & 1 \end{bmatrix}, \quad \begin{bmatrix} \omega & 0 \\ 0 & \omega^2 \end{bmatrix}, \quad \begin{bmatrix} \omega^2 & 0 \\ 0 & \omega \end{bmatrix}, \quad \begin{bmatrix} 0 & 1 \\ 1 & 0 \end{bmatrix}, \quad \begin{bmatrix} 0 & \omega^2 \\ \omega & 0 \end{bmatrix}, \quad \begin{bmatrix} 0 & \omega \\ \omega^2 & 0 \end{bmatrix},$$

where $\omega^3 = 1$, $\omega \neq 1$, form a group of order 6 with respect to matrix multiplication. Prove that this group is isomorphic with that discussed on p. 12.

(12) Show that the identical operation and the rotations through π about any one of three mutually perpendicular intersecting lines form a group of order 4. Construct its multiplication table.

(13) Find the order of each element in the multiplicative group of residues 1, 2, 3, 4, 5, 6 prime to 7. Show that the group is cyclic of order 6, and that it can be generated by 3 and 5, but not by any of the other elements.

Write 5 as a product of two residues of orders 2 and 3 respectively.

(14) Prove that if a finite set of matrices form a group, the latent roots of each matrix are roots of unity.

(15) Show that the set of all matrices

$$A(v) = \left(1 - \frac{v^2}{c^2}\right)^{-\frac{1}{2}} \begin{bmatrix} 1 & -v \\ -\dfrac{v}{c^2} & 1 \end{bmatrix},$$

where v varies in the interval $-c < v < c$, c being a positive constant, form a "continuous" group in the sense that

$$A(v_1)A(v_2) = A(v_3),$$

where $$v_3 = \frac{v_1 + v_2}{1 + \dfrac{v_1 v_2}{c^2}}.$$ **(Lorentz Group)**

ANSWERS. 12. Table 6, p. 21. 13. $5 \equiv 6.2 \pmod{7}$.

CHAPTER II

COMPLEXES AND SUBGROUPS

10. The Calculus of Complexes. In this chapter we shall discuss some general properties of abstract (finite) groups. We imagine that a certain group

$$G : A_1, A_2, \ldots, A_g \qquad . \qquad . \qquad . \qquad (2.1)$$

of order g is given and that all elements with which we are concerned belong to this group. In particular it will be assumed that the *associative law* and the *cancelling rule* (p. 9) have been established once for all.

We shall find it convenient to examine subsets or **complexes** of elements of G. In order to express that a complex K consists of the elements $A, B, C, \ldots$ we use the notation

$$K = A + B + C + \ldots . \qquad . \qquad . \qquad (2.2)$$

We would emphasize that this symbol K does not represent an element of G, but a collection of such elements. The only law of composition for group elements continues to be denoted by the conventional formalism of multiplication, and no element can be regarded as the sum of two elements ; to put it more briefly, the " $+$ " signs in (2.2) stand for the word " and ", and not for " plus ".

A complex is considered completely given if the *distinct* elements occurring in it are known, no account being taken of their order or of duplicates among them ; thus

$$A + B + A + C + B + A = A + B + C = B + A + C = \ldots .$$

We shall learn to manipulate complexes as if they were independent entities, though different in nature from group elements, and we shall establish two laws of composition for complexes, namely, *addition* and *multiplication*.

The **sum** of two complexes K and L is the complex which consists of all elements of K and L combined. Thus if

$$K = K_1 + K_2 + \ldots + K_k \quad \text{and} \quad L = L_1 + L_2 + \ldots + L_l, \quad (2.3)$$
$$K + L = K_1 + \ldots + K_k + L_1 + \ldots + L_l. \quad (2.4)$$

E.g., if $K = A + B + C$ and $L = A + B + D$ we have

$$K + L = A + B + C + D.$$

Addition of complexes is obviously *commutative* and *associative*, i.e.

$$K + L = L + K, \quad (K + L) + M = K + (L + M).$$

Note that

$$K + K = K, \quad \ldots \quad \ldots \quad (2.5)$$

since duplicates of elements are ignored.

The **product** of two complexes is the complex obtained by formal expansion, thus

$$KL = (K_1 + K_2 + \ldots + K_k)(L_1 + L_2 + \ldots + L_l)$$
$$= K_1 L_1 + K_1 L_2 + \ldots + K_k L_l. \quad (2.6)$$

E.g., in the group represented by Table 1, p. 12 we have

$$(I + A + D)(B + D) = B + D + AB + AD + DB + D^2$$
$$= B + D + I + C + C + I = I + B + C + D.$$

If one of the complexes consists of a single element P, we get

$$KP = (K_1 + \ldots + K_k)P = K_1 P + \ldots + K_k P$$

and

$$PK = P(K_1 + \ldots + K_k) = PK_1 + \ldots + PK_k.$$

Multiplication of complexes is in general non-commutative, but it is *associative* and *distributive*, thus

$$K(LM) = (KL)M, \qquad . \qquad . \qquad . \quad (2.7)$$
$$K(L+M) = KL + KM, \qquad . \qquad . \qquad . \quad (2.8)$$
$$(K+L)M = KM + LM. \qquad . \qquad . \qquad . \quad (2.9)$$

These properties follow at once from the definitions.

If each element of K be an element of L, we say K is *contained* in L, and we write

$$K \subset L \quad \text{or} \quad L \supset K;$$

this includes the case in which K and L are in fact identical. Evidently, the two relations

$$K \subset L \quad \text{and} \quad K \supset L$$

hold simultaneously if, and only if,

$$K = L.$$

It is, in general, not permissible to apply the cancelling rule to complexes, i.e. from the equation

$$KL = KM$$

it does *not* follow that

$$L = M. \qquad . \qquad . \qquad . \quad (2.10)$$

However, if one factor be a single element P, we can infer (2.10) whenever

$$PL = PM \quad \text{or} \quad LP = MP \quad . \qquad . \quad (2.11)$$

holds, because (2.11) may be multiplied by P^{-1} on the left or on the right, yielding (2.10) on account of (2.7).

Note that *if* $X \subset K$, *then* $PX \subset PK$ *and* $XQ \subset KQ$ *where P and Q are any elements whatever.*

When, in exceptional cases, two complexes do *commute* we write

$$KL = LK. \qquad . \qquad . \qquad . \quad (2.12)$$

This does *not* mean that every element of K commutes with every element of L; all that is implied by (2.12) is that every element of KL is some element of LK, and *vice versa*, i.e. that every product of the form $K_\alpha L_\beta$ can also be written in the form $L_\rho K_\sigma$ and that every element of the form $L_\gamma K_\delta$ is equal to an element $K_\lambda L_\mu$. In particular, if a complex K commutes with a single element P we have

$$KP = PK,$$

which may also be written

$$P^{-1}KP = K. \quad \text{— } normal \; subgroups$$

Such cases will be of great importance later (Chapter IV).

11. Subgroups. We are particularly interested in those complexes of G whose elements obey the group postulates; such complexes are called **subgroups** of G. Every group G has two trivial or **improper subgroups**, namely, G itself and the group which consists of the unit element by itself $(I^2 = I)$; all other subgroups are called **proper subgroups**. In order that

$$H = (H_1, H_2, \ldots, H_h)$$

be a subgroup of G, its elements must satisfy the fundamental group postulates contained in the definition on p. 2 or, in the case of finite groups, the equivalent requirements laid down in the theorem on p. 9. Since the associative law and the cancelling rule hold for all elements of G, including those of H, it remains only to consider the postulate of closure. Thus we have

THEOREM 1. *A complex H of a finite group G is a subgroup if, and only if, it is closed with respect to multiplication.*

We note that the property of closure *implies* that the unit element of G belongs to H, and that the inverse of every element of H also lies in H.

In the example on p. 12 the complex $H = I + A + B$ is a subgroup of order 3 ; for its closure is made evident by the multiplication table (Table 1) where the nine places, in which the rows and columns headed I, A, B intersect, are occupied solely by the elements I, A, B.

In the calculus of complexes Theorem 1 takes the more concise form :

CRITERION 1. *A complex H of a finite group G is a subgroup if, and only if,*

$$H^2 \subset H. \qquad \qquad (2.13)$$

Proof. (i) The relation (2.13) means that the product of any two elements of H is contained in H, i.e. that H is closed; hence if (2.13) is fulfilled, H is a subgroup. (ii) Conversely, if H is a subgroup, it is closed and therefore (2.13) is true.

It will presently be shown that (2.13) may be replaced by a more precise statement; but we shall first establish the following:

LEMMA 1. *If H be a group and if H be any one of its elements, then*

$$HH = H = HH. \qquad \qquad (2.14)$$

Proof. Since H is closed we have

$$HH \subset H, \qquad \qquad (2.15)$$

where H is any element of H. On the other hand, *the complexes*

$$H = H_1 + H_2 + \ldots + H_h \quad \text{and} \quad HH = H_1 H + H_2 H + \ldots + H_h H$$

contain the same number of elements, because we infer from the cancelling rule that $H_i H \neq H_j H$ unless $H_i = H_j$. Hence we may modify (2.15) and state that $HH = H$. Similarly, we can show that $HH = H$.

COROLLARY. *If H be a group and if C be a complex contained in H, then*

$$HC = H = CH. \qquad \qquad (2.16)$$

For let $C = H' + H'' + \ldots$; then by the lemma

$$HC = HH' + HH'' + \ldots = H + H + \ldots = H$$

on discarding duplicates (see (2.5)).

On applying this result to the case in which $C = H$ we see that, *if H be a group*, $H^2 = H$. Conversely, if this equation be satisfied, we have *a fortiori* $H^2 \subset H$ whence we deduce from Criterion 1 (p. 32) that H is in fact a group. Thus we have established

CRITERION 2. *A complex H of a finite group G is a subgroup if, and only if,*
$$H^2 = H. \qquad . \qquad . \qquad . \qquad (2.17)$$

From a given subgroup it is often possible to derive further subgroups by means of the following theorem:

THEOREM 2. *If H be a subgroup and if P be any element of G, then the complex*
$$H' = P^{-1}HP$$

is a subgroup isomorphic with H, though not necessarily distinct from it.

Proof.   Using Criterion 2 we have by hypothesis $H^2 = H$. Hence
$$(H')^2 = (P^{-1}HP)(P^{-1}HP) = P^{-1}H^2P = P^{-1}HP = H',$$

i.e. H' is a subgroup.

Let $$H = H_1 + H_2 + \ldots + H_h$$

and consider the $(1, 1)$-correspondence
$$H_i' \longleftrightarrow P^{-1}H_iP$$

between the elements of H and H'. An equation of the form
$$H_iH_j = H_k$$

then implies that
$$P^{-1}(H_iH_j)P = P^{-1}H_kP,$$
$$(P^{-1}H_iP)(P^{-1}H_jP) = P^{-1}H_kP,$$
$$H_i'H_j' = H_k',$$

which proves that the two groups are isomorphic (p. 19).

12. Lagrange's Theorem. We begin by a more detailed study of the complexes HX, where H is a subgroup but X is now any element of G, not necessarily contained in H.

LEMMA 2. *If* H *be a subgroup and if* R *and* S *be any two elements of* G, *then the complexes* HR *and* HS *are identical if, and only if,* $RS^{-1} \subset H$; *otherwise they have no element in common.*

Similarly, the complexes RH *and* SH *are identical if, and only if,* $S^{-1}R \subset H$; *otherwise they have no element in common.*

Proof. Let $RS^{-1} = H$, where $H \subset H$. Then by Lemma 1,

$$H(RS^{-1}) = (HR)S^{-1} = H,$$

whence on multiplying by S,

$$HR = HS. \qquad . \qquad . \qquad . \qquad (2.18)$$

Conversely, let us suppose that (2.18) is fulfilled, i.e. that every element of HR is an element of HS, and *vice versa* ; if

$$H = I + H_2 + \ldots + H_h, \qquad . \qquad . \qquad (2.19)$$

a typical element of HR is H_iR ; any one of these elements, including IR, must be of the form H_lS ; thus

$$IR = H_lS,$$
$$RS^{-1} = H_l \subset H.$$

Again, if HR and HS have an element in common, we have an equation of the form

$$H_iR = H_jS,$$
whence
$$RS^{-1} = H_i^{-1}H_j,$$

where the right-hand side represents an element of H because H is a group (a closed set). It then follows from the first part of this proof that the complexes (2.18) are in fact identical.

We are now in a position to prove one of the oldest and most important theorems on groups.

THEOREM 3 (Lagrange). *If* H *is a subgroup of* G *where the orders of these groups are* h *and* g *respectively, then* h *is a factor of* g, *i.e.*

$$g = nh. \qquad . \qquad . \qquad . \qquad (2.20)$$

The integer n *is called the* **index** *of* H *in* G.

There exists a set of n elements $R_1, R_2, \ldots, R_n$ in G such that

$$G = HR_1 + HR_2 + \ldots + HR_n \qquad . \qquad . \quad (2.21)$$

and a set $S_1, S_2, \ldots, S_n$ *such that*

$$G = S_1H + S_2H + \ldots + S_nH. \qquad . \qquad . \quad (2.22)$$

The equations (2.21) *and* (2.22) *are respectively referred to as the decompositions of* G *into* right-hand *or* left-hand **cosets** * *relative to* H.

Proof. The elements $R_1, R_2, \ldots, R_n$ will be determined one by one. Let R_1 be any element of H, e.g., since H is a group, we may put $R_1 = I$. We then have

$$HR_1 = H.$$

If $H \neq G$, there exists an element R_2 of G which is not contained in H. The complexes H and HR_2 cannot be identical because one of the elements of HR_2 is IR_2, i.e. R_2, which is not an element of H. Thus, by Lemma 2, the complexes H and HR_2 have no element in common. Hence the complex

$$HR_1 + HR_2 \qquad . \qquad . \qquad . \qquad . \quad (2.23)$$

contains $2h$ distinct elements of G. If there be an element R_3 of G which is not contained in (2.23), then HR_3, which includes R_3 among its elements, differs from H and HR_2 and therefore has no element in common with either of these complexes. Hence

$$HR_1 + HR_2 + HR_3 \qquad . \qquad . \qquad . \quad (2.24)$$

consists of $3h$ elements of G. If this accounts for all the elements of G we have established the decomposition required $(n = 3)$; in the contrary case, there exists an element R_4 of G which is not contained in (2.24). We then infer that the whole complex HR_4 consists in fact of new elements. Thus at every stage of the proof we

* Sometimes referred to as **associate complexes**.

discover that either the group G has been exhausted or that at least h elements are still left. Since G is finite, this process must come to an end after n steps, say; and we have arrived at the result that

$$G = HR_1 + HR_2 + \ldots + HR_n, \qquad . \qquad . \qquad (2.25)$$

where each of the complexes on the right contains h elements and no two complexes have an element in common. Thus on comparing the number of elements on both sides of (2.25) we find that

$$g = h + h + \ldots + h,$$
$$g = hn.$$

The elements R_i are not uniquely determined; for if H be any element of H whatsoever,

$$HR_i = (HH)R_i = H(HR_i),$$

so that, for our purposes, R_i may be replaced by HR_i.

On the other hand, the aggregate of all distinct complexes of the form HX, where X is any element of G, is of course completely determined by the groups G and H. It is true that we can formally write down g such complexes, namely,

$$HG_1, \quad HG_2, \ldots, \quad HG_g, \qquad . \qquad . \qquad (2.26)$$

where

$$G = G_1 + G_2 + \ldots + G_g.$$

However, if

$$G_\alpha = HG_\beta,$$

where H is any one of the h elements of H, we have

$$HG_\alpha = HG_\beta,$$

so that each complex in (2.26) is repeated h times and only $g/h \ (=n)$ of them are distinct. The n complexes

$$HR_1, \quad HR_2, \ldots, \quad HR_n, \qquad . \qquad . \qquad (2.27)$$

which occur on the right-hand side of (2.25) are actually distinct, and it is for this reason that (2.27) is called a *complete system of right-hand cosets of G relative to H*; it includes as its first member the group H itself. The remaining complexes are not groups because they do not contain the element I.

Similar remarks apply to the *left-hand* cosets YH. By repeating the arguments which led to (2.25) we arrive at a decomposition of the form

$$G = S_1H + S_2H + \ldots + S_nH \qquad . \qquad . \quad (2.28)$$

yielding, as before, the equation

$$g = hn.$$

One of the terms on the right-hand side of (2.28) is equal to H, say

$$S_1H = H,$$

where S_1 is any element of H, e.g., $S_1 = I$.

It should be noted that not only the order h of the subgroup H but also its index $n(=g/h)$ is a factor of g.

Example. In the group of order 6

$$G : I, A, B, C, D, E$$

given in Table 1 (p. 12) the complex

$$H = I + C$$

forms a subgroup of order 2 since $C^2 = I$; or, if we wish to use Criterion 2 (p. 33), because

$$H^2 = (I + C)(I + C) = I + C + C + C^2 = I + C + C + I$$
$$= H + H = H.$$

The index of H in G is 3 $(= 6 \div 2)$ and the elements R_1, R_2, R_3 in (2.25) may be taken as I, A, B respectively; in fact

$$G = H + HA + HB = (I + C) + (I + C)A + (I + C)B$$
$$= I + C + A + D + B + E.$$

We shall now derive some simple consequences of Lagrange's theorem.

COROLLARY 1.   *If* G *be a group of order* g, *the order of every element of* G *is a factor of* g.

Proof.   Let A be an element of G of order a; then G contains the elements

$$I, A, A^2, \ldots, A^{a-1}, \quad (A^a = I)$$

which form a cyclic subgroup of order a. Hence, by Lagrange's theorem, a is a factor of g.

Example.   In the group of Table 1 (p. 12) the elements can only be of orders 1, 2, 3 or 6. In fact, it is easily verified that the orders of I, A, B, C, D, E are 1, 3, 3, 2, 2, 2 respectively.

COROLLARY 2.   *A group of prime order has no proper subgroups and is necessarily cyclic.*

Proof.   If the order of the group be a prime number p, the order of a subgroup must be either 1 or p, i.e. the subgroup consists either of the single element I or contains all p elements of the group.

If A be an element other than I, its order, being greater than 1, is necessarily equal to p. Hence the p elements $I, A, A^2, \ldots, A^{p-1}$ $(A^p = I)$ are all the elements of G in some order.

13. Subgroups of a Cyclic Group.   A cyclic group

$$G = I + A + \ldots + A^{g-1}, \quad (A^g = I)$$

which is generated by the element A, will simply be denoted by

$$G = \{A\}.$$

We can obtain complete information about all its possible subgroups from

THEOREM 4.   *All subgroups of a cyclic group are cyclic. If* {A} *be a cyclic group of order* g, *then corresponding to every divisor* h *of* g *there exists one, and only one, subgroup of order* h, *which may be generated by* $A^{g/h}$.

Proof. (i) Let $g = hn$. The elements

$$I, A^n, A^{2n}, \ldots, A^{(h-1)n} \quad . \quad . \quad . \quad (2.29)$$

are distinct, since an equality between any two of them would lead to a relation

$$A^{ln} = I,$$

where

$$0 < ln < hn(=g).$$

This would contradict the assumption that A is of order g. The elements (2.29) form a cyclic subgroup

$$\{A^n\}$$

of order h, as required.

(ii) Conversely, suppose that

$$H = I + A_1 + A_2 + \ldots + A_{h-1} \quad . \quad . \quad (2.30)$$

is a subgroup of order h of $\{A\}$. Since A_i is an element of $\{A\}$, it must be of the form

$$A_i = A^{\lambda_i},$$

where λ_i is a certain integer such that

$$0 < \lambda_i < g.$$

As H is of order h, the hth power of each of its elements is equal to the unit element. Thus

$$A_i^h = A^{h\lambda_i} = I.$$

It follows that $h\lambda_i$ is a multiple of g (Chapter I, Theorem 3, p. 22), say

$$h\lambda_i = k_i g = k_i hn,$$

whence

$$\lambda_i = k_i n.$$

Hence

$$A_i = A^{\lambda_i} = (A^n)^{k_i},$$

which shows that each element of (2.30) is in fact a power of A^n. But we have seen that not more than h of these powers are distinct, namely the h elements listed in (2.29). Hence the h elements of H in (2.30) are the same as those in (2.29).   Thus

$$H = \{A^n\},$$

which proves the theorem.

We have seen (Corollary 2, p. 38) that groups of prime order have no proper subgroups. The converse of this proposition is also true, namely

THEOREM 5.   *Every finite group of composite order has proper subgroups.*

Proof.   When the group is not cyclic, no single element generates the whole group ; hence if A be any element other than I, then $\{A\}$ is a *proper* subgroup.

In the case of cyclic groups of composite order the existence of proper subgroups is safeguarded by Theorem 4.

14. The H.C.F. and the L.C.M.   The elements that are common to a number of complexes

$$K, L, \ldots \qquad \qquad \qquad (2.31)$$

of G form a complex

$$D = (K, L, \ldots) \qquad \qquad \qquad (2.32)$$

which is called the **intersection** of $K, L, \ldots$.   When the intersection is empty, i.e. when the complexes (2.31) have no element in common we write

$$0 = (K, L, \ldots).$$

It is easy to see that, if P and Q be any elements of G, then

$$PDQ = (PKQ, PLQ, \ldots) \qquad \qquad (2.33)$$

where PDQ is to be interpreted as zero if D is zero.

In order to prove (2.33) let

$$(PKQ, PLQ, \ldots) = D'.$$

If Z' be any element of D', i.e. if

$$Z' \subset PKQ, \quad Z' \subset PLQ, \ldots,$$

we have

$$P^{-1}Z'Q^{-1} \subset K, \quad P^{-1}Z'Q^{-1} \subset L, \ldots,$$

which means that $P^{-1}Z'Q^{-1}$ belongs to D; thus we have shown that $P^{-1}D'Q^{-1} \subset D$, or (see p. 30)

$$D' \subset PDQ. \quad . \quad . \quad . \quad (2.34)$$

In particular, if D is empty so is D'.

Conversely, if Z be any element of D, it follows that PZQ is an element of D', so that

$$PDQ \subset D'. \quad . \quad . \quad . \quad (2.35)$$

The two relations (2.34) and (2.35) together imply (see p. 30) that

$$PDQ = D',$$

which proves (2.33).

We note that, in particular,

$$P^{-1}DP = (P^{-1}KP, P^{-1}LP, \ldots). \quad . \quad . \quad (2.36)$$

When the complexes $K, L, \ldots$ are *subgroups*, their intersection is never empty, as all subgroups have at least the unit element in common. In such cases the intersection is in many respects analogous to the *highest common factor* (**H.C.F.**) of integers and is often called by that name.

THEOREM 6. *The* H.C.F. *(intersection) of subgroups* $A, B, C, \ldots$ *is a subgroup (proper or improper) of each of the groups* $A, B, C, \ldots$.

Proof. Let $D = (A, B, C, \ldots)$. By definition we have

$$D \subset A, \quad D \subset B, \quad D \subset C, \ldots$$

and it only remains for us to prove that D is a group, i.e. that it is closed. If X and Y belong to D, we have

$$X \subset A, \quad X \subset B, \quad X \subset C, \ldots$$

and

$$Y \subset A, \quad Y \subset B, \quad Y \subset C, \ldots$$

Since A is a group it follows that $XY \subset A$, and similarly that $XY \subset B$, $XY \subset C$, ... Hence

$$XY \subset D,$$

which means that D is closed.

Let A, B, ..., F be any elements of G and consider all possible products consisting of a finite number of factors selected from these elements with or without repetitions, e.g. $BAFA^2B$.

The aggregate of all products obtained in this way is denoted by

$$M = \{A, B, \ldots, F\}$$

and is called the *least common multiple* (**L.C.M.**) of A, B, ..., F. From the definition it follows at once that M is *closed* because on multiplying two such products we get another product of a finite number of factors. Every element of M is of course contained in G. Thus we see that M is a subgroup of G; in fact, it is the *smallest* subgroup which includes A, B, ..., F among its elements, since any group which contains these elements necessarily contains all their products and therefore has M as a subgroup.

More generally we may define the L.C.M. of a set of complexes

$$M = \{K, L, \ldots\} \qquad . \qquad . \qquad . \quad (2.37)$$

as the totality of products of a finite number of elements chosen in all possible ways from the elements of K, L, ...

If

$$K = K_1 + K_2 + \ldots, \quad L = L_1 + L_2 + \ldots,$$

and therefore

$$K + L = K_1 + K_2 + \ldots + L_1 + L_2 + \ldots,$$

we may write

$$\{K, L, \ldots\} = \{K_1, K_2, \ldots, L_1, L_2, \ldots\} = \{K + L + \ldots\}. \quad (2.38)$$

A typical element of M may be expressed as

$$X = A_1 A_2 \ldots A_s,$$

where the A's are elements of $K, L, \ldots$ Let P be any element of G and consider the group

$$M' = \{P^{-1}KP, P^{-1}LP, \ldots\}. \qquad . \qquad . \qquad (2.39)$$

Since

$$P^{-1}XP = (P^{-1}A_1P)(P^{-1}A_2P) \ldots (P^{-1}A_sP),$$

we infer that $P^{-1}XP$ belongs to M', as it is a product of elements from $P^{-1}KP, P^{-1}LP, \ldots$ Thus we have shown that

$$P^{-1}MP \subset M'. \qquad . \qquad . \qquad . \qquad (2.40)$$

On reversing the rôles of M and M' where P is to be replaced by P^{-1}, we arrive at the result that

$$PM'P^{-1} \subset M,$$

which together with (2.40) implies that

$$P^{-1}MP = \{P^{-1}KP, P^{-1}LP, \ldots\}. \qquad . \qquad . \qquad (2.41)$$

If

$$G = \{A, B, \ldots, F\}$$

the elements $A, B, \ldots, F$ are said to *generate* the group G.

Thus the group of order 6, whose abstract multiplication table was given on p. 12, can be generated by the two elements A and C, in terms of which each of the six elements can be expressed, namely

$$I = C^2(=A^3), \quad A = A, \quad B = A^2, \quad C = C, \quad D = CA, \quad E = AC.$$

We may therefore denote that group simply by

$$\{A, C\}.$$

However, it must not be supposed that the set of generators is uniquely determined ; for example, in the present case we have

$$\{A, C\} = \{B, D\},$$

since A and C may in turn be expressed in terms of B and D, namely

$$A = B^2, \quad C = DB.$$

It is obvious that every finite group can be generated by a finite number of elements. We say that *the elements*

$$G_1, G_2, \ldots, G_m . \quad . \quad . \quad . \quad (2.42)$$

are **independent** *if none of them can be expressed in terms of the others, i.e. if* G_i *is not an element of* $\{G_1, G_2, \ldots, G_{i-1}, G_{i+1}, \ldots, G_m\}$. A **system of generators** is any set of elements which generate the group. Suppose that

$$G = \{G_1, G_2, \ldots, G_m\}. \quad . \quad . \quad (2.43)$$

We may evidently omit any generator that depends on the others without changing the resulting group (2.43). In fact we can always reduce a given set of generators until they become independent. *Hence every finite group possesses at least one set of independent generators.*

The independence of the generating elements does not preclude the existence of certain relations between them. Thus, returning to our previous example, we can easily verify from the multiplication table (p. 12) that

$$AC = CA^2, \quad \text{or} \quad (AC)^2 = I. \quad . \quad . \quad (2.44)$$

Nevertheless, the elements A and C are independent, as it is clearly impossible to express A in terms of C, or *vice versa*. An equation like (2.44) is called a **defining relation**. *It is often convenient to specify a group by a set of independent generators, for which the associative law is assumed, together with a system of defining relations sufficient to construct the complete multiplication table.*

Thus the group of Table 1 may be given by

$$A^3 = C^2 = (AC)^2 = I, \quad . \quad . \quad (2.45)$$

where the first two relations express that A and C are of orders 3 and 2 respectively. Using only the information contained in (2.45) and the associative law, we might argue as follows : the six elements

$$I, A, A^2, C, CA, CA^2 \quad . \quad . \quad (2.46)$$

are certainly *distinct*, as any equality between them would immediately result in a contradiction; e.g., if A were equal to CA^2, it would follow that $A^{-1} = C$, which is incompatible with the assumption that A and C are independent. On the other hand, the elements (2.46) form a *closed* set in virtue of (2.45); e.g.,

$$(CA)(CA^2) = C(AC)A^2 = CCA^2A^2 = C^2A^4 = A,$$
$$A^2C \quad = A(AC) \quad = ACA^2 \quad = CA^4 \quad = CA,$$

and so on, a factor C being systematically moved to the left until the product is seen to be identical with one of the elements (2.46). The complete multiplication table of these six elements is as follows:

	I	A	A^2	C	CA	CA^2
I	I	A	A^2	C	CA	CA^2
A	A	A^2	I	CA^2	C	CA
A^2	A^2	I	A	CA	CA^2	C
C	C	CA	CA^2	I	A	A^2
CA	CA	CA^2	C	A^2	I	A
CA^2	CA^2	C	CA	A	A^2	I

Table 7

The reader will have no difficulty in convincing himself that this table is identical with Table 1 (p. 12), provided the elements (2.46) are renamed

$$I, A, B, C, D, E$$

respectively.

15. The Direct Product. From any two abstract groups G and H of orders g and h respectively, a new group of order gh may be derived, which is denoted by

$$G \times H \quad \text{or} \quad H \times G$$

and is called the **direct product** of G and H. Its elements are all possible *pairs of elements*, one from G and one from H, and may be written

$$(G, H) \quad \text{or} \quad G \times H \quad \text{or} \quad GH,$$

where G and H are typical elements of G and H respectively. As regards the law of composition it is stipulated that every element of G shall commute with every element of H, and that the elements of G and H shall be completely independent. Thus we have

$$(G_1 H_1)(G_2 H_2) = (G_1 G_2)(H_1 H_2). \qquad (2.47)$$

This rule automatically establishes the *associative law* for the derived group. The *unit element* of $G \times H$ is the product of the unit elements of G and H.

When both G and H are subgroups of a group F, their direct product is isomorphic with $\{G, H\}$ if, and only if,

(i) *every element of G commutes with every element of H*,

(ii) G *and H have only the element I in common.*

It follows that the elements of G and H are then independent in the sense that an equation of the form

$$GH = I, \quad \text{i.e.} \quad G = H^{-1},$$

always implies that $G = I$ and $H = I$.

We see at once from (2.47) that *the direct product of Abelian groups is Abelian.*

More generally we can define the direct product of k groups; it is denoted by

$$G_1 \times G_2 \times \ldots \times G_k ;$$

a typical element may be written

$$\prod_{\lambda=1}^{k} G_\lambda, \qquad (2.48)$$

where G_λ is a typical element of G_λ. The factors in (2.48) commute with one another and are independent in the sense that

$$\prod_{\lambda=1}^{k} G_\lambda = I$$

if, and only if, each G_λ is equal to the unit element.

Example. The least positive residues prime to the modulus 15 are

$$1, 2, 4, 7, 8, 11, 13, 14. \qquad . \qquad . \qquad (2.49)$$

They form an Abelian group of order 8 (pp. 15-18) which, as we shall now show, is equivalent to the direct product of two cyclic groups generated by the elements 2 and 11 respectively. In fact the residue 2 generates a cyclic group of order 4, namely

$$C_4 : 1, 2, 4, 8 ; \quad 2^4 = 16 \equiv 1 \pmod{15}.$$

Similarly, 11 generates a cyclic group of order 2,

$$C_2 : 1, 11 ; \quad 11^2 = 121 \equiv 1 \pmod{15}.$$

The elements of $C_4 \times C_2$ are obtained by multiplying the elements of C_4 by those of C_2, thus

$$C_4 \times C_2 : 1, 2, 4, 8, 11, 22, 44, 88.$$

On being reduced to the least positive residue relative to 15, these numbers become

$$1, 2, 4, 8, 11, 7, 14, 13,$$

which agrees with (2.49). The group is therefore isomorphic with $C_4 \times C_2$.

The following lemma will be used in the next section, but is also of some intrinsic interest :

LEMMA 3. *If each element of* G, *other than the unit element, be of order* 2, *then* G *is Abelian and isomorphic with*

$$C_2 \times C_2 \times \ldots \times C_2.$$

Its order is a power of 2.

Proof. The proposition is obviously true when G is the (only) group of order 2. Suppose then that the order of G is greater than 2 and let A and B be any two distinct elements other than I. We have

$$A^2 = I, \quad \text{i.e.} \quad A = A^{-1}$$

and

$$B^2 = I, \quad \text{i.e.} \quad B = B^{-1}.$$

Next consider the element AB. Evidently $AB \neq I$, or else $A = B^{-1} = B$. Hence, by hypothesis, AB is of order 2, i.e.

$$I = (AB)^2 = A(BA)B,$$
$$BA = A^{-1}B^{-1} = AB,$$

which proves that G is Abelian.

Like every finite group G possesses a finite set of independent generators, say

$$A_1, A_2, \ldots, A_k.$$

Since the group is Abelian, powers of the same element may be collected in any product. Thus the general element of G can be written

$$G = A_1^{\alpha_1} A_2^{\alpha_2} \ldots A_k^{\alpha_k},$$

where $\alpha_i = 0$ or 1 $(i = 1, 2, \ldots, k)$, because the square of each element is equal to I. Hence

$$G = \{A_1\} \times \{A_2\} \times \ldots \times \{A_k\},$$

and the order of G is

$$g = 2 \times 2 \times \ldots \times 2 = 2^k.$$

16. Survey of Groups up to Order 8. No successful method has yet been discovered for constructing all possible abstract groups of preassigned order, nor do we know in advance how many such groups exist, except in a few simple cases.

The modest means with which we have so far furnished the reader will, however, suffice to give a complete list of groups up to order 8. We shall specify each of these groups by a set of defining relations. Since groups of prime order have already been discussed (Corollary 2, p. 38), it only remains for us to consider in more detail the cases in which

$$g = 4 \quad \text{or} \quad 6 \quad \text{or} \quad 8.$$

There are two groups of order 4, both of them Abelian.

For if $g = 4$, any element, other than I, can only be of order 4 or 2 (Corollary 1, p. 38).

(1) If G contains an element A of order 4, this element generates G ; in fact the four elements of G can be written

$$I, A, A^2, A^3, (A^4 = I) \quad . \quad . \quad . \quad (2.50)$$

and we have $G = C_4$, a cyclic group of order 4.

(2) Next, suppose that every element, except I, is of order 2. Hence by Lemma 3 (p. 47)

$$G = C_2 \times C_2,$$

i.e. G is generated by two elements A and B, and the four elements of G can be written

$$I, A, B, AB, \quad . \quad . \quad . \quad . \quad (2.51)$$

where

$$A^2 = B^2 = I, \quad AB = BA. \quad . \quad . \quad . \quad (2.52)$$

This group is called the **four-group** or **quadratic group** (F. Klein's " *Vierergruppe* ") ; it is often denoted by V.

There being no other possibilities, we conclude that *any group of order 4 is isomorphic either with C_4 or with V*. We have already encountered both these groups in Chapter I. In fact, Table 5 (p. 20) represents C_4 since $B = A^2$, $C = A^3$, while Table 6 (p. 21) corresponds to V, provided we write $C = AB$.

There are two groups of order 6, one cyclic and one non-Abelian.

(1) If G possesses an element A of order 6, then

$$G = \{A\} = C_6.$$

(2) Next, suppose there is no element of order 6 ; the order of every element, other than I, is therefore either 2 or 3 (Corollary 1, p. 38). Since the order of G is not a power of 2, not all its elements can be of order 2 (Lemma 3, p. 47). Hence there exists at least one element A of order 3, so that

$$I, A, A^2 \quad (A^3 = I) \quad . \quad . \quad . \quad (2.53)$$

are three distinct elements of G. If B be a further element, it is easy to see that the six elements

$$I, A, A^2, B, AB, A^2B \quad . \quad . \quad . \quad (2.54)$$

are distinct, because an equality between any two of them would immediately lead to a contradiction; e.g. $A^2B = A$ would imply that $B = A^{-1} = A^2$, whereas we had supposed that B was not one of the elements (2.53). If the set (2.54) is to form a group of order 6, the condition of closure must be fulfilled. In particular, B^2 must be equal to one of the elements (2.54); as we cannot have an equation of the form $B^2 = A^iB$ (it would be incompatible with the independence of A and B), there are only the following three possibilities

$$\text{(a) } B^2 = I, \quad \text{(b) } B^2 = A, \quad \text{(c) } B^2 = A^2. \quad . \quad (2.55)$$

In the last two cases B would be of order 3, i.e. $B^3 = I$; but on post-multiplying (b) or (c) by B we should get $I = AB$ or $I = A^2B$, neither of which can possibly be true. Thus it follows that (a) must hold, i.e.

$$B^2 = I. \quad . \quad . \quad . \quad (2.56)$$

Next consider the element BA; it must be contained in (2.54). As it cannot be equal to B or to a power of A, we are left with the alternatives

$$\text{(a) } BA = AB, \quad \text{(b) } BA = A^2B. \quad . \quad (2.57)$$

In the first case G would be Abelian, in which case

$$(AB)^2 = A^2B^2 = A^2 \neq I, \quad (AB)^3 = A^3B^3 = B \neq I,$$

and the element AB would be of order 6, contrary to the assumption made at the beginning of this section. Thus we are forced to conclude that

$$BA = A^2B, \quad \text{i.e. } (AB)^2 = I.$$

Subject to the associative law being confirmed, the relations

$$A^3 = B^2 = (AB)^2 = I \quad . \quad . \quad . \quad (2.58)$$

completely define the group which we first introduced in Table 1 and have repeatedly discussed since, especially in Table 7 (see (2.45), p. 45). There are no other groups of order 6.

There are five groups of order 8 of which three are Abelian and two are non-Abelian.

Three Abelian groups of order 8 are easily written down, namely :

(1) $C_8 = \{A\}$, where $A^8 = I$ (Table 8, p. 54).
(2) $C_4 \times C_2 = \{A, B\}$, where $A^4 = B^2 = I$, $AB = BA$
$$\text{(Table 9, p. 54).}$$
(3) $C_2 \times C_2 \times C_2 = \{A, B, C\}$, where $A^2 = B^2 = C^2 = I$,
$$AB = BA, BC = CB, CA = AC \quad \text{(Table 10, p. 55).}$$

In searching for further groups of order 8 we may assume that the maximum order of elements is less than 8 and greater than 2 (Lemma 3, p. 47). Hence there is at least one element A of order 4, i.e.

$$A^4 = I, \qquad . \qquad . \qquad . \qquad (2.59)$$

and any element other than I is either of order 2 or 4.

If B be an element not contained in $\{A\}$, we can write the eight elements of the group in the form

$$I, A, A^2, A^3, B, AB, A^2B, A^3B. \quad . \qquad (2.60)$$

The condition of closure demands that B^2 be one of these elements, which in fact must be one of the first four, since B is independent of A. But the equations

$$B^2 = A \quad \text{or} \quad B^2 = A^3$$

are impossible, as they would imply that the order of B was neither 2 nor 4. Thus there remain only two possibilities, namely

$$\text{(4) } B^2 = I \quad \text{or} \quad \text{(5) } B^2 = A^2.$$

(4) Assume that $B^2 = I$. The product BA must be equal to one of the last three elements of (2.60).

(a) If $BA = AB$, we obtain the Abelian group which has already been noted under (2).

(b) The relation $BA = A^2B$, which is equivalent to

$$B^{-1}A^2B = A,$$

is impossible, as on squaring we should arrive at the result

$$A^2 = (B^{-1}A^2B)(B^{-1}A^2B) = B^{-1}A^4B = B^{-1}IB = I,$$

in contradiction to (2.59). Thus we are forced to the conclusion that

(c) $\qquad\qquad BA = A^3B, \quad \text{or} \quad (AB)^2 = I.$

The group which is defined by the relations

$$A^4 = B^2 = (AB)^2 = I \qquad . \qquad . \qquad . \quad (2.61)$$

is called the **dihedral group** *of order 8* (Table 11, p. 55), or **octic group**.

It belongs to a class of groups which we shall discuss later (p. 90), when the associative law will be confirmed.

(5) Let $B^2 = A^2$. In this case B is, like A, of order 4. Again, BA must be equal to one of the last three elements of (2.60).

(a) If $BA = AB$, the group is Abelian. On putting $C = AB^{-1}$ we see that C is of order 2. Also, since $B = C^{-1}A$, A and C may be taken as generating elements of the group, which is therefore of the form $C_4 \times C_2$ (type (2)).

(b) The relation $BA = A^2B$, i.e. $BA = B^2B = B^3$, is impossible, as it would imply that $A = B^2 = A^2$, which is clearly absurd. Thus we must assume that

(c) $\qquad\qquad BA = A^3B.$

The relations

$$A^4 = I, \quad A^2 = B^2, \quad BA = A^3B \qquad . \quad .. \quad (2.62)$$

do in fact define what is called the **quaternion group** (Table 12, p. 55).

In order to explain this name we remind the reader that a quaternion is a *hypercomplex number*

$$a_0 + a_1 i + a_2 j + a_3 k,$$

where the coefficients a_0, a_1, a_2, a_3, are *real* numbers, and the four *units*

$$1, i, j, k \qquad \cdots \qquad (2.63)$$

satisfy the relations

$$i^2 = j^2 = -1, \quad ij = -ji = k. \qquad \cdot \qquad (2.64)$$

If we are only interested in the multiplicative properties of the symbols (2.63), we must interpret -1 as i^2, and the rules (2.64), which govern the algebra of quaternions, become $k = ij$ and

$$i^4 = 1, \quad i^2 = j^2, \quad ji = i^3 j. \qquad \cdots \qquad (2.65)$$

In this form they are indeed identical with (2.62), apart from the notation.

The reader will have no difficulty in demonstrating that the quaternion group is isomorphic with the groups of matrices generated by

$$A_2 = \begin{bmatrix} 0 & \sqrt{-1} \\ \sqrt{-1} & 0 \end{bmatrix} \quad \text{and} \quad B_2 = \begin{bmatrix} 0 & 1 \\ -1 & 0 \end{bmatrix},$$

or by

$$A_4 = \begin{bmatrix} 0 & 1 & 0 & 0 \\ -1 & 0 & 0 & 0 \\ 0 & 0 & 0 & -1 \\ 0 & 0 & 1 & 0 \end{bmatrix} \quad \text{and} \quad B_4 = \begin{bmatrix} 0 & 0 & 1 & 0 \\ 0 & 0 & 0 & 1 \\ -1 & 0 & 0 & 0 \\ 0 & -1 & 0 & 0 \end{bmatrix}.$$

This affords an indirect verification of the associative law, which is known to be true for all matrices.

The quaternion group is an instance of a **dicyclic group**. These are groups of order $4m$ defined by

$$A^{2m} = I \quad , \quad A^m = (AB)^2 = B^2 \quad .$$

The elements of a dicyclic group may be written

$$I, A, \ldots, \quad A^{2m-1}, \quad B, \quad AB, \ldots, \quad A^{2m-1}B.$$

The square of every element which does not belong to $\{A\}$, is equal to B^2. For since

$$ABA = B,$$
$$(A^xB)^2 = A^xBA^xB = A^{x-1}(ABA)A^{x-1}B = A^{x-1}BA^{x-1}B$$
$$= A^{x-2}(ABA)A^{x-2}B = A^{x-2}BA^{x-2}B$$
$$= \ldots = A^0BA^0B = B^2.$$

To emphasize the structural difference of the five possible groups of order 8 we append their complete multiplication tables:

$$C_8 = \{A\}, \quad A^8 = I.$$

	I	A	A^2	A^3	A^4	A^5	A^6	A^7
I	I	A	A^2	A^3	A^4	A^5	A^6	A^7
A	A	A^2	A^3	A^4	A^5	A^6	A^7	I
A^2	A^2	A^3	A^4	A^5	A^6	A^7	I	A
A^3	A^3	A^4	A^5	A^6	A^7	I	A	A^2
A^4	A^4	A^5	A^6	A^7	I	A	A^2	A^3
A^5	A^5	A^6	A^7	I	A	A^2	A^3	A^4
A^6	A^6	A^7	I	A	A^2	A^3	A^4	A^5
A^7	A^7	I	A	A^2	A^3	A^4	A^5	A^6

Table 8

$$C_4 \times C_2 = \{A, B\}, \quad A^4 = B^2 = I.$$

	I	A	A^2	A^3	B	AB	A^2B	A^3B
I	I	A	A^2	A^3	B	AB	A^2B	A^3B
A	A	A^2	A^3	I	AB	A^2B	A^3B	B
A^2	A^2	A^3	I	A	A^2B	A^3B	B	AB
A^3	A^3	I	A	A^2	A^3B	B	AB	A^2B
B	B	AB	A^2B	A^3B	I	A	A^2	A^3
AB	AB	A^2B	A^3B	B	A	A^2	A^3	I
A^2B	A^2B	A^3B	B	AB	A^2	A^3	I	A
A^3B	A^3B	B	AB	A^2B	A^3	I	A	A^2

Table 9

$$C_2 \times C_2 \times C_2 = \{A, B, C\}, \quad A^2 = B^2 = C^2 = I.$$

	I	A	B	C	AB	AC	BC	ABC
I	I	A	B	C	AB	AC	BC	ABC
A	A	I	AB	AC	B	C	ABC	BC
B	B	AB	I	BC	A	ABC	C	AC
C	C	AC	BC	I	ABC	A	B	AB
AB	AB	B	A	ABC	I	BC	AC	C
AC	AC	C	ABC	A	BC	I	AB	B
BC	BC	ABC	C	B	AC	AB	I	A
ABC	ABC	BC	AC	AB	C	B	A	I

Table 10

Dihedral Group $A^4 = B^2 = I$, $BA = A^3B$.

	I	A	A^2	A^3	B	AB	A^2B	A^3B
I	I	A	A^2	A^3	B	AB	A^2B	A^3B
A	A	A^2	A^3	I	AB	A^2B	A^3B	B
A^2	A^2	A^3	I	A	A^2B	A^3B	B	AB
A^3	A^3	I	A	A^2	A^3B	B	AB	A^2B
B	B	A^3B	A^2B	AB	I	A^3	A^2	A
AB	AB	B	A^3B	A^2B	A	I	A^3	A^2
A^2B	A^2B	AB	B	A^3B	A^2	A	I	A^3
A^3B	A^3B	A^2B	AB	B	A^3	A^2	A	I

Table 11

Quaternion Group $A^4 = I$, $A^2 = B^2$, $BA = A^3B$.

	I	A	A^2	A^3	B	AB	A^2B	A^3B
I	I	A	A^2	A^3	B	AB	A^2B	A^3B
A	A	A^2	A^3	I	AB	A^2B	A^3B	B
A^2	A^2	A^3	I	A	A^2B	A^3B	B	AB
A^3	A^3	I	A	A^2	A^3B	B	AB	A^2B
B	B	A^3B	A^2B	AB	A^2	A	I	A^3
AB	AB	B	A^3B	A^2B	A^3	A^2	A	I
A^2B	A^2B	AB	B	A^3B	I	A^3	A^2	A
A^3B	A^3B	A^2B	AB	B	A	I	A^3	A^2

Table 12

17. The Product Theorem. At the beginning of this chapter (2.6) we defined the product of two complexes, K and L. We shall now examine the case in which both these complexes are *subgroups* of G. It will appear that the product of two subgroups (when both are regarded as complexes) is not always a subgroup.

THEOREM 7 (Product Theorem). *If A and B be subgroups of orders a and b respectively, with an intersection (H.C.F.) of order d, then the complex*

$$C = AB$$

contains exactly ab/d *distinct elements; and C is a group if, and only if, A and B commute.*

Proof. (i) Since A and B are groups, their intersection D is a subgroup of either group (Theorem 6, p. 41), and we can decompose B into cosets relative to D, thus

$$B = DB_1 + DB_2 + \ldots + DB_n, \qquad . \qquad . \quad (2.66)$$

where $n = b/d$ and

$$DB_i \neq DB_j, \quad \text{if } i \neq j. \qquad . \qquad . \qquad . \quad (2.67)$$

Multiplying (2.66) on the left by A we obtain

$$AB = ADB_1 = ADB_2 + \ldots + ADB_n.$$

Since D is contained in A, it follows from the Corollary on p. 32 that $AD = A$, and therefore

$$AB = AB_1 + AB_2 + \ldots + AB_n. \qquad . \qquad . \quad (2.68)$$

Each complex AB_i contains a distinct elements, and no two of these complexes have an element in common; for, if they had, we should get an equation of the form

$$A_\alpha B_i = A_\beta B_j, \quad (i \neq j)$$

where A_α and A_β are certain elements of A. Hence it would follow that

$$A_\beta{}^{-1} A_\alpha = B B_i{}^{-1}. \qquad . \qquad . \qquad . \quad (2.69)$$

Since A is closed the left-hand side of (2.69) would be an element of A; similarly, the right-hand side would represent an element of B. This element would therefore be common to A and B, i.e. it would belong to the intersection D. Hence, by Lemma 1, we should have

$$D(B_jB_i^{-1}) = D,$$
$$DB_j = DB_i$$

in contradiction to (2.67). Thus we conclude that the complexes AB_i in (2.68) have no elements in common and therefore contain a total of

$$na = \frac{b}{d}a$$

distinct elements. This proves the first part of the theorem. On interchanging A and B we note that *the complexes* AB *and* BA (*where* A *and* B *are groups*) *always contain the same number of elements even when* $AB \neq BA$.

(ii) Next, suppose that the complex $C = AB$ is in fact a group. If A and B be any elements of A and B respectively, we have $A^{-1} \subset A$, $B^{-1} \subset B$ and therefore

$$A^{-1}B^{-1} \subset AB.$$

Since AB is a group it contains the reciprocal of $A^{-1}B^{-1}$, i.e.

$$(A^{-1}B^{-1})^{-1} = BA \subset AB.$$

Now BA may be considered a typical element of BA. Hence we have proved that

$$BA \subset AB.$$

On the other hand, we have just seen that these two complexes contain the same number of distinct elements, so that BA cannot be a proper part of AB; it therefore follows that

$$BA = AB. \quad . \quad . \quad . \quad . \quad (2.70)$$

E

(iii) Conversely, if (2.70) is true, we have

$$C^2 = (AB)(AB) = A(BA)B = A(AB)B$$
$$= A^2B^2 = AB = C,$$

using Criterion 2 (p. 33) for the groups A and B; and in virtue of the same Criterion we infer that C is a group. This completes the proof of the Product Theorem.

NOTE : This theorem is analogous to a well-known result of elementary arithmetic, namely that if a and b be any two integers whose H.C.F. and L.C.M. are d and c respectively, then

$$c = ab/d.$$

18. Decomposition relative to Two Subgroups. The decomposition of a group into cosets (Lagrange's Theorem, p. 34) was essentially based on the fact that two such cosets are either identical or else have no element in common. Whenever a set of complexes possesses this property, the elements of G can be divided into mutually exclusive classes.

The following generalization of the concept of cosets is due to G. Frobenius.*

Let A and B be subgroups of G (which need not be distinct) of orders a and b respectively, and consider complexes of the form

$$APB, \ AQB, \ \ldots$$

where $P, Q, \ldots$ are any elements of G. We shall prove that if two such complexes have one element in common, they are in fact identical. Indeed, let us suppose

$$A_1PB_1 = A_2QB_2,$$

where A_1, A_2 are elements of A and B_1, B_2 of B. On premultiplying by A and postmultiplying by B, we find that

$$AA_1PB_1B = AA_2QB_2B. \quad . \quad . \quad (2.71)$$

---

* *Sitzungsberichte Berlin*, 1895, pt. i, pp. 163-94.

Since A and B are groups we have (Lemma 1, p. 32)

$$AA_1 = AA_2 = A,$$
$$B_1B = B_2B = B,$$

whence (2.71) becomes

$$APB = AQB.$$

We note that the complex APB contains the element IPI, i.e. P.

Using these facts, we can obtain a decomposition of G in the following way : choose any element P_1 of G. If the complex AP_1B is less than G, let P_2 be an element not contained in it. Since P_2 is an element of AP_2B but not of AP_1B, these two complexes have no element in common, and we can segregate from G the complex

$$AP_1B + AP_2B. \qquad . \qquad . \qquad . \qquad (2.72)$$

If there be an element P_3 not yet accounted for, the complex AP_3B consists entirely of new elements and should be added to (2.72). We proceed in this way until the whole group G is exhausted. No further elements can then be found and we have an equation of the form

$$G = AP_1B + AP_2B + \ldots + AP_rB. \qquad . \qquad (2.73)$$

We say that G *has been decomposed relative to the subgroups A and B*.

In contrast to the resolution into cosets, the number of elements in the various terms on the right-hand side of (2.73) may vary and requires closer examination. Consider a typical complex

$$AP_\rho B = K_1 + K_2 + \ldots + K_l$$

which contains, say, l distinct elements of G. Evidently the complex

$$P_\rho{}^{-1}AP_\rho B = P_\rho{}^{-1}K_1 + P_\rho{}^{-1}K_1 + \ldots + P_\rho{}^{-1}K_l \qquad (2.74)$$

also contains l distinct elements, because if

$$P_\rho^{-1} K_\alpha = P_\rho^{-1} K_\beta$$

we should find that

$$K_\alpha = K_\beta,$$

and *vice-versa*.   Let

$$P_\rho^{-1} A P_\rho = A_\rho.$$

This is a subgroup which is isomorphic with **A** (Theorem 2, p. 33) and hence is of order a.   The left-hand side of (2.74) can accordingly be regarded as the product of two groups, namely

$$A_\rho B.$$

On applying the Product Theorem (p. 56) we infer that

$$l = ab/d_\rho, \qquad . \qquad . \qquad . \qquad . \quad (2.75)$$

where d_ρ is the order of the intersection (A_ρ, B).

We collect these results in the following theorem.

THEOREM 8 (Frobenius).   *If **A** and **B** are subgroups of **G** of orders* a *and* b *respectively, **G** admits of a decomposition into mutually exclusive complexes relative to **A** and **B**, thus*

$$G = AP_1 B + AP_2 B + \ldots + AP_r B.$$

The complex $AP_\rho B$ *contains* ab/d_ρ *elements where* d_ρ *is the order of the intersection* $(P_\rho^{-1} A P_\rho, B)$.

COROLLARY.   *On counting the number of elements in each term of* (2.73) *we obtain the relation*

$$g = \sum_{\rho=1}^{r} \frac{ab}{d_\rho}. \qquad . \qquad . \qquad . \quad (2.76)$$

Examples

(1) If H is a subgroup and K any complex of **G**, prove that $HK = H$ or $KH = H$ implies that $K \subset H$.

(2) Let $D = (X, Y)$ and $M = \{X, Y\}$ where X and Y are any complexes.   If Z be another complex, show that

$$(X, Y, Z) = (D, Z) \quad \text{and} \quad \{X, Y, Z\} = \{M, Z\}.$$

(3) If A and B be subgroups whose orders are relatively prime, prove that their intersection consists only of the unit element.

(4) Prove that if $G = HR_1 + HR_2 + \ldots + HR_n$ is a decomposition of G into right-hand cosets relative to a subgroup H, then $G = R_1^{-1}H + R_2^{-1}H + \ldots + R_n^{-1}H$ is a decomposition into left-hand cosets.

(5) Find all subgroups of order 4 of the dihedral group of order 8 (Table 11).

(6) Show that the group of Table 1 (p. 12) may be defined by the relations $C^2 = D^2 = (CD)^3 = I$.

(7) Prove that there are only two non-commutative groups of order 12 which contain an element of order 6, and that they are defined by the relations

(i) $A^6 = B^2 = (AB)^2 = I$ and (ii) $A^6 = I$, $B^2 = (AB)^2 = A^3$

respectively.

(8) Show that the residues prime to 21 form an Abelian group with respect to multiplication which is isomorphic with $C_6 \times C_2$.

(9) A certain group of order 16 is defined by $A^4 = B^2 = C^2 = (AB)^2 = I$, $AC = CA$, $BC = CB$. Show that $H = I + B + C + BC$ and $K = I + A^2 + C + A^2C$ form subgroups of order 4. Find a decomposition of G into right-hand cosets (i) relative to H and (ii) relative to K. Verify that H and K commute, and obtain the subgroup of order 8 represented by their product. Of what type is it ?

(10) Show that the group of the preceding example is the direct product of the octic group and the group $\{C\}$.

HINTS and ANSWERS. 5. $\{A\}$, $\{A^2, B\}$, $\{AB, A^3B\}$. 7. The elements $B^{-1}AB$ and B^2 must be powers of A, the former being of order 6. Transform the latter by B. 9. $C_2 \times C_2 \times C_2$.

CHAPTER III

GROUPS OF PERMUTATIONS

19. The Symmetric Group P_n. The operation of re-arranging n distinct objects amongst themselves is called a **permutation of degree** n. The objects will be denoted by letters or simply by the numerals

$$1, 2, \ldots, n. \qquad \cdots \qquad (3.1)$$

If the permutation A replaces 1 by a_1, 2 by $a_2, \ldots, n$ by a_n, where

$$a_1, a_2, \ldots, a_n \qquad \cdots \qquad (3.2)$$

are the numbers (3.1) in some order, we shall write

$$A = \begin{pmatrix} 1 & 2 & \ldots & n \\ a_1 & a_2 & \ldots & a_n \end{pmatrix} \qquad \cdots \qquad (3.3)$$

to indicate that each number in the first row is to be replaced by the number immediately below it in the second row.

There are as many different permutations of n objects as there are arrangements * of the type (3.2).

From elementary Algebra it is known that this number is equal to $n!$

Since it is immaterial in what order the information about the n objects is given, we may rearrange the columns of the symbol (3.3) at will; indeed it is always possible to modify the expression for A in such a way that the first row consists of the numbers 1, 2, ..., n in any preassigned

---

* We use the word " arrangement " to denote the *sequence* of numbers (3.2), reserving the term " permutation " for the *operation* which replaces (3.1) by (3.2).

order, provided the same pairs are kept in vertical align-
ment as in (3.3). Thus each of the $n!$ permutations can
be written in $n!$ different forms. E.g.

$$\begin{pmatrix} 1 & 2 & 3 & 4 \\ 2 & 3 & 1 & 4 \end{pmatrix} = \begin{pmatrix} 2 & 1 & 4 & 3 \\ 3 & 2 & 4 & 1 \end{pmatrix} = \begin{pmatrix} 4 & 2 & 1 & 3 \\ 4 & 3 & 2 & 1 \end{pmatrix} = \cdots$$

By the *product* AB we mean the permutation obtained by
first carrying out A and then * B. Suppose that

$$B = \begin{pmatrix} 1 & 2 & \ldots & n \\ b_1 & b_2 & \ldots & b_n \end{pmatrix} = \begin{pmatrix} a_1 & a_2 & \ldots & a_n \\ c_1 & c_2 & \ldots & c_n \end{pmatrix}, \quad (3.4)$$

where the second symbol for B has been derived from the
first by rearranging the columns until the first row becomes
identical with the second row in the symbol (3.3) for A.
This has been done to prepare B for premultiplication by A.
We now have

$$AB = \begin{pmatrix} 1 & 2 & \ldots & n \\ a_1 & a_2 & \ldots & a_n \end{pmatrix} \begin{pmatrix} a_1 & a_2 & \ldots & a_n \\ c_1 & c_2 & \ldots & c_n \end{pmatrix}$$

$$= \begin{pmatrix} 1 & 2 & \ldots & n \\ c_1 & c_2 & \ldots & c_n \end{pmatrix}; \quad (3.5)$$

for a typical number i is changed by A into a_i, and B
changes a_i into c_i; hence the combined effect of A and B
(in this sequence) is to change i into c_i, which agrees with
the final symbol in (3.5). Notice that when the second
factor B has been prepared for multiplication by A, the
product AB is found simply by placing the second row of
B below the first row of A. E.g., if

$$A = \begin{pmatrix} 1 & 2 & 3 & 4 \\ 2 & 3 & 4 & 1 \end{pmatrix} \quad \text{and} \quad B = \begin{pmatrix} 1 & 2 & 3 & 4 \\ 3 & 1 & 2 & 4 \end{pmatrix},$$

$$AB = \begin{pmatrix} 1 & 2 & 3 & 4 \\ 2 & 3 & 4 & 1 \end{pmatrix} \begin{pmatrix} 2 & 3 & 4 & 1 \\ 1 & 2 & 4 & 3 \end{pmatrix} = \begin{pmatrix} 1 & 2 & 3 & 4 \\ 1 & 2 & 4 & 3 \end{pmatrix}.$$

On the other hand,

$$BA = \begin{pmatrix} 1 & 2 & 3 & 4 \\ 3 & 1 & 2 & 4 \end{pmatrix} \begin{pmatrix} 3 & 1 & 2 & 4 \\ 4 & 2 & 3 & 1 \end{pmatrix} = \begin{pmatrix} 1 & 2 & 3 & 4 \\ 4 & 2 & 3 & 1 \end{pmatrix},$$

* Some authors adhere to the opposite convention.

which shows that multiplication of permutations is, in general, *not* commutative.

With a little practice the reader will become accustomed to evaluate products without having to write out the intermediate stage of preparation. Thus in the example we have just considered the product BA may be found as follows : 1 is moved to 3 by B, and 3 is moved to 4 by A ; hence by combining these operations we see that BA moves 1 to 4. Next, 2 is moved to 1 by B, and 1 is moved to 2 by A ; hence 2 is moved to 2 (is left unaltered) by BA, and so on. Having defined the multiplication of permutations, we shall now prove

THEOREM 1. *The set of all permutations of* n *objects forms a group* P_n *of order* n! ; *it is called the* **symmetric group** *of degree* n.

Proof. We shall verify postulates (I) to (IV) of Chapter I, pp. 1-2.

(i) The *closure* of the set P_n of all permutations of n objects follows immediately from the definition of multiplication.

(ii) To prove the *associative law* let us contract the symbol for permutations and write

$$A = \begin{pmatrix} \alpha \\ \beta \end{pmatrix},$$

where α is a typical representative of the numbers 1, 2, ..., n and β is its image under the operation A. Similarly, we may assume that, after being suitably prepared, two further permutations may be represented by

$$B = \begin{pmatrix} \beta \\ \gamma \end{pmatrix}, \quad C = \begin{pmatrix} \gamma \\ \delta \end{pmatrix}.$$

We then have

$$(AB)C = \left\lceil \begin{pmatrix} \alpha \\ \beta \end{pmatrix} \begin{pmatrix} \beta \\ \gamma \end{pmatrix} \right\rceil \begin{pmatrix} \gamma \\ \delta \end{pmatrix} = \begin{pmatrix} \alpha \\ \gamma \end{pmatrix} \begin{pmatrix} \gamma \\ \delta \end{pmatrix} = \begin{pmatrix} \alpha \\ \delta \end{pmatrix}$$

and

$$A(BC) = \begin{pmatrix} \alpha \\ \beta \end{pmatrix} \left[\begin{pmatrix} \beta \\ \gamma \end{pmatrix} \begin{pmatrix} \gamma \\ \delta \end{pmatrix} \right] = \begin{pmatrix} \alpha \\ \beta \end{pmatrix} \begin{pmatrix} \beta \\ \delta \end{pmatrix} = \begin{pmatrix} \alpha \\ \delta \end{pmatrix},$$

i.e. $$(AB)C = A(BC).$$

(iii) The *unit element* of P_n is the "identical" permutation

$$I = \begin{pmatrix} 1 & 2 & \ldots & n \\ 1 & 2 & \ldots & n \end{pmatrix} = \ldots = \begin{pmatrix} a_1 & a_2 & \ldots & a_n \\ a_1 & a_2 & \ldots & a_n \end{pmatrix},$$

which leaves each object unchanged.

(iv) If

$$A = \begin{pmatrix} 1 & 2 & \ldots & n \\ a_1 & a_2 & \ldots & a_n \end{pmatrix},$$

the *inverse* permutation may be represented by

$$A^{-1} = \begin{pmatrix} a_1 & a_2 & \ldots & a_n \\ 1 & 2 & \ldots & n \end{pmatrix}.$$

Indeed, in contracted notation, we have

$$AA^{-1} = \begin{pmatrix} \lambda \\ a_\lambda \end{pmatrix} \begin{pmatrix} a_\lambda \\ \lambda \end{pmatrix} = \begin{pmatrix} \lambda \\ \lambda \end{pmatrix} = I$$

and

$$A^{-1}A = \begin{pmatrix} a_\lambda \\ \lambda \end{pmatrix} \begin{pmatrix} \lambda \\ a_\lambda \end{pmatrix} = \begin{pmatrix} a_\lambda \\ a_\lambda \end{pmatrix} = I.$$

This concludes the proof of the theorem.

Suppose the objects $1, 2, \ldots, n$ have been separated into two mutually exclusive sets, say

$$\alpha_1, \alpha_2, \ldots, \alpha_\nu; \quad \beta_1, \beta_2, \ldots, \beta_{n-\nu}.$$

If A permutes only the α's amongst themselves and if B operates only on the β's, then the order in which A and B are carried out is evidently irrelevant, since neither operation has an influence on the other. *Hence two per-*

mutations which operate on mutually exclusive sets of objects always commute. E.g., if

$$A = \begin{pmatrix} 1 & 2 & 3 & 4 \\ 2 & 1 & 3 & 4 \end{pmatrix} \quad \text{and} \quad B = \begin{pmatrix} 1 & 2 & 3 & 4 \\ 1 & 2 & 4 & 3 \end{pmatrix},$$

$$AB = BA = \begin{pmatrix} 1 & 2 & 3 & 4 \\ 2 & 1 & 4 & 3 \end{pmatrix},$$

since A operates only on 1, 2 and B only on 3, 4.

20. Circular Permutations (Cycles). A permutation which interchanges the objects cyclically is called a **circular permutation** or **cycle**. Thus if m objects be denoted by $1, 2, \ldots, m$, such a permutation is represented by

$$C = \begin{pmatrix} 1 & 2 & \ldots & m-1 & m \\ 2 & 3 & \ldots & m & 1 \end{pmatrix}. \qquad . \qquad . \quad (3.6)$$

If we visualize the m objects arranged at m places on the circumference of a circle, the permutation C moves each object to the next place so that the last object comes to occupy the place of the first.

On account of their great importance for the theory of permutations, cycles are usually written in contracted notation thus

$$C = (1 \ 2 \ \ldots \ m),$$

indicating that each number in the bracket is to be replaced by its successor on the right, and the last number by the first. Since it is immaterial with which number we begin, we have

$$(1 \ 2 \ \ldots, m) = (2 \ 3 \ \ldots \ m \ 1)$$
$$= (3 \ 4 \ \ldots \ m \ 1 \ 2) = (m \ 1 \ \ldots \ m-1). \quad (3.7)$$

We shall now prove

THEOREM 2. *Every permutation can be uniquely resolved into cycles which operate on mutually exclusive sets of objects.*

Proof. Let A be a given permutation of $1, 2, \ldots, n$. Beginning with any one of these integers, say λ, let us suppose that A moves λ to λ', λ' to λ'', λ'' to λ''', and so on ; as there are only n numbers involved in A, there must be an index r, where $1 \leqslant r \leqslant n$ such that

$$\lambda^{(r)} = \lambda.$$

Thus some part of the effect of A is equivalent to the cycle

$$L = (\lambda \ \lambda' \ \lambda'' \ \ldots \ \lambda^{(r)}). \quad \cdot \quad \cdot \quad \cdot \quad (3.8)$$

If $r = n$, all numbers have been accounted for and we have $A = L$. On the other hand, if $r < n$, let μ be a number not contained in L and suppose that A carries μ into μ', μ' into μ'', and so on until we return to μ, as we must do after at most $n - r$ steps ; for the images of μ and its successors are certainly different from the λ's, or else two numbers, one μ and one λ, would have the same image. We have therefore isolated another cycle

$$M = (\mu \ \mu' \ \mu'' \ \ldots \ \mu^{(s)}),$$

say. If $r + s = n$ we have proved that $A = LM = ML$ (see the remark at the end of § 19, p. 65).

On the other hand, if $r + s < n$, the process may be continued, and more cycles are extracted from A until finally each of the n objects has been drawn into one of the cycles. Thus we get a decomposition of A :

$$A = (\lambda \ \lambda' \ \ldots \ \lambda^{(r)})(\mu \ \mu' \ \ldots \ \mu^{(s)}) \ \ldots \ (\rho \ \rho' \ \ldots \ \rho^{(u)}), \quad (3.9)$$

where

$$r + s + \ldots + u = n. \quad \cdot \quad \cdot \quad \cdot \quad (3.10)$$

This resolution into mutually exclusive cycles is *unique*, save for the order in which the cycles occur (we have already seen that they all commute), and save for the alternative ways in which each cycle may be expressed (see 3.7) ; for it is clear that two essentially different products of cycles correspond to different permutations.

Example :

$$\begin{pmatrix} 1 & 2 & 3 & 4 & 5 & 6 & 7 & 8 \\ 4 & 5 & 2 & 8 & 3 & 6 & 1 & 7 \end{pmatrix} = (1 \ 4 \ 8 \ 7)(2 \ 5 \ 3)(6).$$

A cycle which consists of a single letter merely indicates that this letter is unaltered ; such cycles are often omitted, it being understood that any letter which is not explicitly mentioned, remains unchanged.* When this convention is adopted, the complete interpretation of a product of cycles depends on the degree (n) of the permutation, i.e. on the number of objects involved.

Thus $(1\ 2\ 3) = \begin{pmatrix} 1 & 2 & 3 \\ 2 & 3 & 1 \end{pmatrix}$, when $n = 3$,

$(1\ 2\ 3) = \begin{pmatrix} 1 & 2 & 3 & 4 & 5 \\ 2 & 3 & 1 & 4 & 5 \end{pmatrix}$, when $n = 5$.

It is easy to write down the powers of a given cycle

$$C = (1\ 2\ \ldots\ m).$$

Since C moves every letter to the next place on the circumference of a circle, C^2 sends every letter two places along, C^3 three places along, and so on. Generally, C^k replaces x by $x + k$ where this number has to be reduced to its least positive remainder relative to m. In particular, it follows that C is of order m, i.e.

$$(1\ 2\ \ldots\ m)^m = I, \qquad . \qquad . \qquad . \quad (3.11)$$

because C^m replaces x by $x + m$, which is equivalent to x. *Thus a cycle of degree* m *is of order* m. E.g., when $m = 6$, we have

$$(1\ 2\ 3\ 4\ 5\ 6)^2 = (1\ 3\ 5)(2\ 4\ 6)$$
$$(1\ 2\ 3\ 4\ 5\ 6)^3 = (1\ 4)(2\ 5)(3\ 6)$$
$$(1\ 2\ 3\ 4\ 5\ 6)^4 = (1\ 5\ 3)(2\ 6\ 4)$$
$$(1\ 2\ 3\ 4\ 5\ 6)^5 = (1\ 6\ 5\ 4\ 3\ 2)$$
$$(1\ 2\ 3\ 4\ 5\ 6)^6 = I.$$

Let

$$P = C_1 C_2 \ldots C_r \qquad . \qquad . \qquad . \quad (3.12)$$

* The identical permutation I is then usually written (1) to save it from total evanescence.

be the resolution of a given permutation into mutually exclusive cycles of orders

$$\mu_1, \mu_2, \ldots, \mu_r \, . \qquad . \qquad . \qquad . \quad (3.13)$$

respectively. Since these cycles commute we have (see (1.7))

$$P^m = C_1{}^m C_2{}^m \ldots C_r{}^m.$$

Suppose now that P is of order m so that

$$C_1{}^m C_2{}^m \ldots C_r{}^m = I, \qquad . \qquad . \qquad . \quad (3.14)$$

and therefore

$$C_1{}^m = (C_2 C_3 \ldots C_r)^{-m}.$$

Now C_2, C_3, $\ldots$, C_r do not permute the letters which are involved in C_1. Hence

$$C_1{}^m = I.$$

Similarly, we prove that $C_2{}^m = C_3{}^m = \ldots = C_r{}^m = I.$ It follows that m is a multiple of each of the integers (3.13). Thus *the order of any permutation is the L.C.M. of the orders of its component (mutually exclusive) cycles.*

A permutation is said to be **regular** if all its cycles are of the same degree.

As an example we give a list of the six permutations of P_3 ($n = 3$), each resolved into cycles :

$$I = (1), \quad A = (1\ 2\ 3), \quad B = (1\ 3\ 2),$$
$$C = (1\ 2), \quad D = (1\ 3), \quad E = (2\ 3).$$

We have

$$A^3 = (1\ 2\ 3)^3 = I, \quad C^2 = (1\ 2)^2 = I, \quad (AC)^2 = (2\ 3)^2 = I.$$

Comparing these relations with (2.45) p. 44, we see that P_3 is isomorphic with the abstract group of Table 1, see p. 12. Thus the elements of that group may be interpreted or **represented** as permutations, and all relations which follow from the multiplication table have their counterpart in relations between the permutations of the group P_3. This affords an indirect verification of the associative law for the abstract group under consideration (p. 12), because this law is known to hold for all permutations, and in particular for P_3.

21. Classes of Permutations. Two permutations, A and B of degree n, are said to be **similar** or **conjugate** * *with respect to* P_n if there exists a permutation T in P_n such that

$$B = T^{-1}AT. \quad . \quad . \quad . \quad (3.15)$$

This concept is of fundamental importance in the theory of groups and will be more fully discussed in the next chapter.

The relation between two conjugate permutations is best understood when they are resolved into cycles. Let

$$A = C_1 C_2 \ldots C_r \quad . \quad . \quad . \quad (3.16)$$

be a given permutation decomposed into r mutually exclusive cycles, and let

$$T = \begin{pmatrix} 1 & 2 & \ldots & n \\ 1' & 2' & \ldots & n' \end{pmatrix} = \begin{pmatrix} \lambda \\ \lambda' \end{pmatrix}$$

be any permutation of P_n whatsoever. We wish to find an expression for $T^{-1}AT$. Since

$$T^{-1}AT = (T^{-1}C_1 T)(T^{-1}C_2 T) \ldots (T^{-1}C_r T), \quad (3.17)$$

it is sufficient to evaluate a typical factor

$$T^{-1}CT,$$

where

$$C = (a_1\, a_2 \ldots a_m) = \begin{pmatrix} a_i \\ a_{i+1} \end{pmatrix} \quad . \quad . \quad (3.18)$$

is a cycle of degree m. (In the last symbol a_{m+1} must be considered identical with a_1.) Generally we can write

---

* This agrees with the terminology of Chapter IV. In a different context, some authors speak of conjugate permutations when we should use the terms ' *reciprocal* ' or ' *inverse* ' (A. C. Aitken, *Determinants and Matrices*, 4th ed., p. 33).

$$T^{-1} = \begin{pmatrix} \lambda' \\ \lambda \end{pmatrix}.$$

If λ does not occur in C, then λ' is not altered by the permutation $T^{-1}CT$. For T^{-1} transforms λ' into λ which is changed back into λ' by T, the factor C having remained passive. On the other hand, if $\lambda = a_i$, we have

$$a_i' \longrightarrow a_i \text{ (by } T^{-1}), \quad a_i \longrightarrow a_{i+1} \text{ (by } C),$$
$$a_{i+1} \longrightarrow a_{i+1}' \text{ (by } T),$$

so that $T^{-1}CT$ changes a_i' into a_{i+1}'. Thus we can write

$$T^{-1}CT = (a_1' \; a_2' \ldots a_m'). \qquad . \qquad . \quad (3.19)$$

On comparing (3.18) with (3.19) we observe that $T^{-1}CT$ *is derived from C by applying the permutation T to the letters in the bracket representing C.* This rule holds generally for any product of cycles. E.g., if

$$A = (1 \; 3)(2 \; 4 \; 5) \quad \text{and} \quad T = \begin{pmatrix} 1 & 2 & 3 & 4 & 5 \\ 2 & 4 & 5 & 1 & 3 \end{pmatrix}$$

we have

$$T^{-1}AT = (2 \; 5)(4 \; 1 \; 3)$$

replacing, in the expression for A, 1 by 2, 3 by 5, ... as required by T.

Let us suppose that in (3.16) the cycles are arranged in *non-decreasing* order, including those of order 1, and let these orders be denoted by

$$1 \leqslant \mu_1 \leqslant \mu_2 \leqslant \ldots \leqslant \mu_r \leqslant n, \quad . \qquad . \quad (3.20)$$

where

$$\mu_1 + \mu_2 + \ldots + \mu_r = n. \qquad . \qquad . \quad (3.21)$$

Thus every permutation of degree n is associated with a **partition** of n into positive integers, namely, the degrees of the cycles into which it is decomposed. *Two permutations which correspond to the same partition are said to belong to the same* **class** * *of* P_n. It follows from (3.16) and (3.17) that

---

* Not to be confused with the distinction between even and odd permutations (p. 74 below). The word '*class*' will not be used by us in this connexion.

conjugate permutations belong to the same class. Conversely, if A and B be two permutations of the same class, say

$$A = (a_1 \ldots a_{\mu_1})(b_1 \ldots b_{\mu_2}) \ldots (u_1 \ldots u_{\mu_r})$$

and

$$B = (\alpha_1 \ldots \alpha_{\mu_1})(\beta_1 \ldots \beta_{\mu_2}) \ldots (\omega_1 \ldots \omega_{\mu_r}),$$

then a permutation T can be found such that

$$B = T^{-1}AT. \qquad \qquad (3.22)$$

Indeed if we put

$$T = \begin{pmatrix} a_1 \ldots a_{\mu_1} \; b_1 \ldots b_{\mu_2} \ldots u_1 \ldots u_{\mu_r} \\ \alpha_1 \ldots \alpha_{\mu_1} \; \beta_1 \ldots \beta_{\mu_2} \ldots \omega_1 \ldots \omega_{\mu_r} \end{pmatrix},$$

the evaluation of the product on the right-hand side of (3.22) amounts to replacing the letters in the cycles of A by the corresponding Greek letters, a process which turns A into B. Thus we have proved the important result :

THEOREM 3. *Two permutations are conjugate with respect to* P_n *if, and only if, they belong to the same class.*

There are clearly as many classes of P_n as there are different ways of partitioning n in accordance with (3.20) and (3.21). It is important to know how many permutations belong to a given class. Instead of specifying the class by a partition (3.21), let us suppose that each of its members involves

$$\alpha_1 \text{ cycles of degree } 1,$$
$$\alpha_2 \text{ cycles of degree } 2,$$
$$\ldots\ldots\ldots\ldots\ldots\ldots$$
$$\alpha_n \text{ cycles of degree } n,$$

where

$$1\alpha_1 + 2\alpha_2 + \ldots + n\alpha_n = n. \qquad \qquad (3.23)$$

The set of *non-negative* integers

$$(\alpha) : \alpha_1, \alpha_2, \ldots, \alpha_n \qquad \qquad (3.24)$$

completely determines the *class* (α). To construct all permutations of (α) imagine a pattern of empty brackets

$$\underbrace{(\cdot)(\cdot) \ldots (\cdot)}_{\alpha_1}\underbrace{(\cdot \cdot)(\cdot \cdot) \ldots (\cdot \cdot)}_{\alpha_2} \ldots \quad . \quad (3.25)$$

which correspond precisely to the cycles of a typical permutation A of (α). There are altogether n blank spaces in the pattern, and these can be filled with the letters $1, 2, \ldots, n$ in $n!$ ways. However, not all these $n!$ arrangements correspond to distinct permutations. For the α_k cycles of degree k $(k = 1, 2, \ldots, n)$ may be permuted in any manner without causing a change in the resulting permutation A. Thus the same permutation is obtained

$$\alpha_1! \, \alpha_2! \ldots \alpha_n! \, . \quad . \quad . \quad . \quad (3.26)$$

times if all $n!$ arrangements are considered. Also, it should be remembered that a cycle of degree k may be written in k different ways since each of its letters may be brought to the leading position in the bracket (p. 66). Hence α_k cycles of degree k admit of k^{α_k} equivalent arrangements of letters yielding the same permutation

$$1^{\alpha_1} \cdot 2^{\alpha_2} \cdot \ldots n^{\alpha_n} \quad . \quad . \quad . \quad (3.27)$$

times. Thus in order to obtain the exact number h_α of cycles in the class (α), we must divide $n!$ by (3.26) and (3.27). This gives the formula

$$h_\alpha = \frac{n!}{1^{\alpha_1}\alpha_1! \; 2^{\alpha_2}\alpha_2! \ldots n^{\alpha_n}\alpha_n!} \; , \quad . \quad (3.28)$$

which is due to Cauchy.*

22. Transpositions. A cycle of the form (ab) is called a transposition ; it interchanges the letters a and b and leaves all the others unaltered. We note that (see (3.11))

$$(ab)^2 = I, \quad (ab) = (ab)^{-1} = (ba).$$

Let

$$x_1, x_2, \ldots, x_n$$

be independent variables and consider the *product of differences*

* *Exercice d'analyse et de physique mathématique*, iii (1844), p. 173.

$$\left.\begin{aligned}
\Delta = (x_1 - x_2)(x_1 - x_3)(x_1 - x_4) \dots (x_1 - x_n) \\
\cdot \ (x_2 - x_3)(x_2 - x_4) \dots (x_2 - x_n) \\
\cdot \ (x_3 - x_4) \dots (x_3 - x_n) \\
\cdots \\
\cdot \ (x_{n-1} - x_n)
\end{aligned}\right\} \quad (3.29)$$

If the variables be subjected to a permutation A, the function Δ is formally changed into a new function Δ_A which is, however, identically equal either to Δ or to $-\Delta$. We shall write

$$\Delta_A = \zeta(A)\Delta, \quad . \quad . \quad . \quad (3.30)$$

where $\zeta(A)$ is a function of the permutation A which has the property that

$$\zeta(A) = 1 \text{ or } -1. \quad . \quad . \quad (3.31)$$

DEFINITION 1. *A permutation* A *is said to be* **even** *or* **odd** *according as* $\zeta(A) = 1$ *or* $\zeta(A) = -1$. *The function* $\zeta(A)$ *is called the* **alternating character** *of* P_n. The most important fact about this function is expressed in the following :

THEOREM 4. *If* A *and* B *be any two permutations,*

$$\zeta(AB) = \zeta(A)\zeta(B) ; \quad . \quad . \quad (3.32)$$

i.e. the product of two even or two odd permutations is even whilst the product of an even and an odd permutation is odd.

Proof. If we apply the permutation B to both sides of (3.30), we get

$$\Delta_{AB} = \zeta(A)\Delta_B = \zeta(A)\zeta(B)\Delta. \quad . \quad . \quad (3.33)$$

On the other hand, if we let the permutation AB take the place of A, the identity (3.30) becomes

$$\Delta_{AB} = \zeta(AB)\Delta, \quad . \quad . \quad . \quad (3.34)$$

whence we deduce (3.32) by comparing (3.33) and (3.34).

Evidently, if I is the identical permutation, we have $\Delta_I \equiv \Delta$, i.e.

$$\zeta(I) = 1. \quad . \quad . \quad . \quad (3.35)$$

Hence, on putting $A = B^{-1}$ in (3.32), we find that

$$\zeta(B)\zeta(B^{-1}) = 1, \qquad \qquad (3.36)$$

or in view of (3.31)

$$\zeta(B) = \zeta(B^{-1}). \qquad \qquad (3.37)$$

Also, if A and B be any two permutations, we have by a repeated application of (3.32)

$$\zeta(B^{-1}AB) = \zeta(B^{-1})\zeta(A)\zeta(B) = \zeta(B^{-1})\zeta(B)\zeta(A),$$

whence by (3.36)

$$\zeta(B^{-1}AB) = \zeta(A), \qquad \qquad (3.38)$$

i.e. permutations of the same class have the same alternating character.

THEOREM 5. *All transpositions are odd permutations.*

Proof. Let $A = (12)$. The function $\Delta_{(12)}$ is obtained from Δ by an interchange of x_1 and x_2. We see by inspection of (3.29) that this amounts to reversing the sign of each difference in the first two rows, thus

$$\Delta_{(12)} = (-1)^{n-1}(-1)^{n-2}\Delta = -\Delta,$$

i.e.

$$\zeta((12)) = -1.$$

To obtain the alternating character of other transpositions we use the identities

$$(1a) = (2a)(12)(2a)^{-1}, \quad (a > 2), \qquad . \qquad (3.39)$$

$$(ab) = (1b)(1a)(1b)^{-1}, \quad (1 < a < b), . \qquad (3.40)$$

whence by (3.38)

$$\zeta((ab)) = \zeta((1a)) = \zeta((12)),$$

and therefore

$$\zeta((ab)) = -1$$

for all transpositions.

THEOREM 6. *Every permutation can, in infinitely many ways, be expressed as a product of transpositions, the number of transpositions in such a product being always even or always odd according as the given permutation is even or odd.*

Proof. We shall first show that every cycle can be expressed as a product of transpositions ; indeed

$$(a_1 \, a_2 \ldots a_m) = (a_1 \, a_2)(a_1 \, a_3) \ldots (a_1 \, a_m), \quad . \quad (3.41)$$

as can be verified by evaluating the product on the right-hand side : $a_1 \longrightarrow a_2, a_2 \longrightarrow a_1 \longrightarrow a_3, a_3 \longrightarrow a_1 \longrightarrow a_4,$ and so on.

Since every permutation can be written as a product of cycles, the first part of the theorem is proved. As the transpositions in (3.41) have a letter in common, they do not, in general, commute. Also, the product is not changed by the insertion of pairs of factors such as

$$(ab)(ab),$$

which are equivalent to the identical permutation. For this reason alone the factorization into transpositions cannot be unique.

Suppose that a given permutation A is expressed as a product of transpositions in any way whatever,

$$A = T_1 T_2 \ldots T_s. \quad . \quad . \quad . \quad (3.42)$$

By Theorems 4 and 5 we have

$$\zeta(A) = \prod_{i=1}^{s} \zeta(T_i) = (-1)^s.$$

Hence the number of factors in (3.42) is even or odd according as A is even or odd.

We see from (3.40) that every transposition can be expressed in terms of the special transpositions $(1k)$, where $k = 2, 3, \ldots, n$. Using the technical term introduced in Chapter II, p. 43, we may enunciate

THEOREM 7. *The symmetric group* P_n *may be generated by the* n – 1 *transpositions*

$$(12), (13), \ldots, (1n). \quad . \quad . \quad . \quad (3.43)$$

23. The Alternating Group A_n. We return to the distinction between even and odd permutations introduced on p. 74.

THEOREM 8. *In any group of permutations G either all or exactly half the permutations are even. The even permutations of G form a group by themselves.*

Proof. If G contains no odd permutation, there is nothing to prove. Suppose that Q is an odd permutation belonging to G so that $\zeta(Q) = -1$. As X runs through the whole group, so does QX where Q is fixed (p. 32). Hence

$$\sum_X \zeta(X) = \sum_X \zeta(QX).$$

On the other hand,

$$\sum \zeta(QX) = \sum \zeta(Q)\zeta(X) = -\sum \zeta(X),$$

whence

$$\sum \zeta(X) = 0.$$

This means that the sum contains an equal number of positive and negative terms, i.e. there are as many even as odd permutations in G. Also, it is evident from Theorem 4 that the even permutations of G obey the postulate of closure and therefore form a (proper or improper) subgroup of G.

Special interest is attached to the case in which G is the symmetric group P_n.

DEFINITION 2. *The set of all even permutations of degree* n *forms a group* A_n *of order* $\frac{1}{2}n!$, *which is called the* **alternating group** *of degree* n.

E.g., the alternating group A_4 is of order $\frac{1}{2}(4!)$, i.e. 12, and consists of the following permutations (arranged according to classes of P_4) :

$\quad$ (1) $(=I)$

A_4 : $(1\ 2)(3\ 4)$, $\quad(1\ 3)(2\ 4)$, $\quad(1\ 4)(2\ 3)$

$\qquad(1\ 2\ 3)$, $\quad(1\ 2\ 4)$, $\quad(1\ 3\ 2)$, $\quad(1\ 3\ 4)$, $\quad(1\ 4\ 2)$,

$\qquad\qquad\qquad\qquad(1\ 4\ 3)$, $\quad(2\ 3\ 4)$, $\quad(2\ 4\ 3)$.

A permutation is even if, and only if, it can be written as the product of an even number of transpositions. By Theorem 7 these transpositions may be selected from the set (3.43) and then arranged in pairs. Since

$$(1i)(1j) = (1ij) \quad (i \neq j, \, i > 1, \, j > 1),$$

we have

THEOREM 9. *The alternating group* A_n *may be generated by the* n – 2 *ternary cycles*

$$(1 \; 2 \; 3), \, (1 \; 2 \; 4), \, \ldots, \, (1 \; 2 \; n). \qquad (3.44)$$

24. Cayley's Theorem. It was not until comparatively late that the abstract concept of a group was fully appreciated. The earlier literature on the subject, including the classical works of Cauchy, Galois and Jordan,* dealt exclusively with groups of permutations, although they contain many results which apply equally well to all finite groups. A close study of permutation groups is, however, of more than historical interest, because we shall presently show that every finite group whatsoever is isomorphic with a suitable group of permutations. This important fact was discovered by A. Cayley.†

Let

$$\mathsf{G} : G_1, G_2, \ldots, G_g \qquad (3.45)$$

be an abstract group of order g. If P be any one of these elements, the products

$$G_1P, G_2P, \ldots, G_gP \qquad (3.46)$$

are g distinct elements of G and therefore represent a rearrangement of (3.45). Thus with every element P of G we can associate a permutation of degree g, namely

$$P' = \begin{pmatrix} G_1 & G_2 & \ldots & G_g \\ G_1P & G_2P & \ldots & G_gP \end{pmatrix}. \qquad (3.47)$$

---

* C. Jordan, *Traité des substitutions*, Paris 1870.
† *Phil. Mag.* vol. vii (**4**), 1854, pp. 40-47.

The objects on which this permutation operates are the group elements themselves. It is convenient to use the abbreviated notation

$$P' = \begin{pmatrix} G_i \\ G_iP \end{pmatrix} \quad (i = 1, 2, \ldots, g). \qquad . \qquad . \quad (3.48)$$

When G_i runs through the whole group, so does G_iX where X is a fixed element of G. The information contained in (3.48) may therefore also be expressed by

$$P' = \begin{pmatrix} G_iX \\ G_iXP \end{pmatrix}. \qquad . \qquad . \qquad . \quad (3.49)$$

Similarly, let

$$Q' = \begin{pmatrix} G_i \\ G_iQ \end{pmatrix} \qquad . \qquad . \qquad . \quad (3.50)$$

be the permutation corresponding to the element Q. If P and Q are distinct, the permutations (3.48) and (3.50) are certainly not equal; indeed, since $G_iP \neq G_iQ$, they have a different effect on each of the permuted objects. Hence we have established a $(1, 1)$-*correspondence* between the elements $P, Q, \ldots$ of G and the set (3.48) of permutations $P', Q', \ldots$.

Next, let us evaluate the product $P'Q'$; we find that

$$P'Q' = \begin{pmatrix} G_i \\ G_iP \end{pmatrix}\begin{pmatrix} G_i \\ G_iQ \end{pmatrix} = \begin{pmatrix} G_i \\ G_iP \end{pmatrix}\begin{pmatrix} G_iP \\ G_iPQ \end{pmatrix} = \begin{pmatrix} G_i \\ G_iPQ \end{pmatrix}.$$

The result is the permutation which corresponds to the group element PQ; i.e. we have

$$(PQ)' = P'Q'. \qquad . \qquad . \qquad . \quad (3.51)$$

Thus we have shown that the correspondence

$$P \longleftrightarrow P'$$

is in fact an *isomorphism*. The set of permutations of degree g

$$\mathsf{G}' : P', Q', \ldots$$

forms a group (a subgroup of P_g) which possesses the same structure as the given abstract group G.

The permutation which corresponds to I is evidently the identical permutation

$$I' = \begin{pmatrix} G_i \\ G_i I \end{pmatrix} = \begin{pmatrix} G_i \\ G_i \end{pmatrix}.$$

Any other permutation of **G'** displaces each group element since it changes G_i into $G_i P$, which differs from G_i unless $P = I$.

We shall now resolve P' into cycles. Let the corresponding abstract element be of order r, thus

$$P^r = I. \qquad . \qquad . \qquad . \qquad (3.52)$$

Beginning with any element G of **G**, we know that it is changed by P' into GP, which in turn is changed into GP^2 ; the image of GP^2 under P' is GP^3, and so on until we come to GP^{r-1} which is transformed into GP^r, i.e. into G, in virtue of (3.52). Thus we see that P' contains the cycle

$$(G, GP, GP^2, \ldots, GP^{r-1}) \qquad . \qquad . \qquad (3.53)$$

of order r. If H be an element of **G** not included in (3.53), we can isolate a further cycle of P', namely

$$(H, HP, HP^2, \ldots, HP^{r-1}),$$

which is likewise of order r. This process is to be continued until all elements of **G** have been accounted for. We have then arrived at the resolution

$$P' = (G, GP, \ldots, GP^{r-1})(H, HP, \ldots, HP^{r-1}) \ldots$$
$$(L, LP, \ldots, LP^{r-1}),$$

which shows that P' is a *regular* permutation (p. 69).

We may summarize our results as follows :

THEOREM 10 (Cayley).   *With each element* P *of an abstract group*

$$\textbf{G} : G_1, G_2, \ldots, G_g,$$

we can associate a regular permutation

$$P' = \begin{pmatrix} G_1 & G_2 & \ldots & G_g \\ G_1 P & G_2 P & \ldots & G_g P \end{pmatrix}.$$

The set of all these permutations forms a group G' (subgroup of P_g) which is isomorphic with G; i.e. if $P \longleftrightarrow P'$ and $Q \longleftrightarrow Q'$, then $PQ \longleftrightarrow P'Q'$.

When an abstract group G is isomorphic with a group G' whose elements are concrete mathematical entities such as permutations or matrices, we say that G' is a **faithful representation** of G in terms of permutations or matrices, as the case may be. All properties of G are also possessed by G'. Conversely, any information about G' which does not really depend on the special nature of its elements, applies equally to G. The idea of representing an abstract group by concrete elements is in some respects analogous to the use of co-ordinates in the treatment of geometrical problems ; it carries with it the same analytical advantages and aesthetic blemishes.

The permutation group G' which, according to Cayley's Theorem, may be associated with an abstract group G is called the **regular representation** of G.

It is quite possible that an abstract group may admit of more than one faithful representation in terms of permutations which may even be of different degrees. E.g., consider the group

$$G : I, A, B, C, D, E \qquad . \qquad . \qquad (3.54)$$

of Table 1 (p. 12). To obtain its regular representation we postmultiply the set by each of the elements in turn, thereby transforming it into the various columns of the multiplication table. In this way the regular permutations can immediately be written down, namely

$$I' = \begin{pmatrix} I & A & B & C & D & E \\ I & A & B & C & D & E \end{pmatrix} = (I)(A)(B)(C)(D)(E)$$

$$A' = \begin{pmatrix} I & A & B & C & D & E \\ A & B & I & D & E & C \end{pmatrix} = (I\ A\ B)(C\ D\ E)$$

$$B' = \begin{pmatrix} I & A & B & C & D & E \\ B & I & A & E & C & D \end{pmatrix} = (I\ B\ A)(C\ E\ D)$$

$$C' = \begin{pmatrix} I & A & B & C & D & E \\ C & E & D & I & B & A \end{pmatrix} = (I \ C)(A \ E)(B \ D)$$

$$D' = \begin{pmatrix} I & A & B & C & D & E \\ D & C & E & A & I & B \end{pmatrix} = (I \ D)(A \ C)(B \ E)$$

$$E' = \begin{pmatrix} I & A & B & C & D & E \\ E & D & C & B & A & I \end{pmatrix} = (I \ E)(A \ D)(B \ C)$$

On the other hand, as we have seen on p. 69, the same group may be faithfully represented by the six permutations of P_3, which operates only on three symbols.

25. Transitive Groups. In this and the following section we shall consider permutations of a fixed degree n, i.e. we shall be concerned with subgroups G of the symmetric group P_n. The objects on which G operates will again be denoted by $1, 2, \ldots, n$ or by letters $\alpha, \beta, \ldots$.

DEFINITION 3. *A group of permutations is said to be* **transitive** *if it contains at least one permutation which transforms any one of the* n *letters into any other letter. Otherwise the group is said to be* **intransitive**.

Note that this concept applies to groups of permutations only.

Let a permutation which changes α into β be denoted by $P_{\alpha\beta}$ irrespective of the effect it has on the remaining letters. We note that $P_{\alpha\beta}^{-1}$ changes β into α. There may of course be more than one such permutation for a given pair α, β.

Evidently the symmetric group P_n is transitive, as it contains all possible permutations, including the transposition $(\alpha\beta)$ which transforms α into β.

On the other hand, the group

$$V_1 : \quad (1), \quad (1 \ 2), \quad (3 \ 4), \quad (1 \ 2)(3 \ 4)$$

of order and degree 4 is intransitive because none of its permutations changes 1 into 3. Incidentally, this group is isomorphic with the group

$$V_2 : \quad (1), \quad (1 \ 2)(3 \ 4), \quad (1 \ 3)(2 \ 4), \quad (1 \ 4)(2 \ 3)$$

which, on the contrary, is transitive. Both groups are isomorphic with the four-group ((2.52), p. 49).

The set of permutations of G which leave the first symbol (1) unaltered forms a subgroup G_1; for the identical permutation certainly belongs to this set, as does the product of any two of its members. <u>Generally, we denote by G_α the subgroup of all permutations of G which leave the letter α unaltered.</u>

THEOREM 11. *A group of permutations G of degree* n *is transitive if, and only if, the subgroup* G_1 *is of index* n *relative to* G.

Proof. (i) Suppose that G is transitive. By hypotheses it contains permutations

$$P_{11}, P_{12}, \ldots, P_{1n} \qquad . \qquad . \qquad . \quad (3.55)$$

which transform 1 into 1, 2, ..., n respectively. We shall prove that the n complexes

$$G_1 P_{11}, G_1 P_{12}, \ldots, G_1 P_{1n} . \qquad . \qquad . \quad (3.56)$$

are in fact a complete system of cosets of G relative to G_1. The complexes (3.56) are distinct because the letter 1 is transformed differently by permutations belonging to different complexes. For let Q be any permutation of G whatsoever and suppose that Q changes 1 into α, say. Since $P_{1\alpha}^{-1}$ changes α back into 1, the permutation $QP_{1\alpha}^{-1}$ leaves 1 invariant and accordingly belongs to G_1, thus

$$QP_{1\alpha}^{-1} \subset G_1, \quad Q \subset G_1 P_{1\alpha}.$$

Hence the complexes (3.56) comprise the whole group, i.e. G_1 is of index n.

(ii) Conversely, if G_1 be of index n, let

$$G = G_1 R_1 + G_1 R_2 + \ldots + G_1 R_n$$

be the decomposition of G into cosets relative to G_1. It is easy to see that no two of the permutations

$$R_1, R_2, \ldots, R_n . \qquad . \qquad . \qquad . \quad (3.57)$$

transform 1 into the same symbol; for if R_i and R_j were to change 1 into the same letter α, the permutation $R_iR_j^{-1}$ would leave 1 unaltered and would therefore belong to G_1. By Chapter II, Lemma 2 (p. 34), this would imply that $G_1R_i = G_1R_j$, which is impossible. Hence the permutations (3.57) may in some order be taken for the permutations (3.55) whose existence has thus been established.

Finally, if α and β be any two of the n letters of G, the permutation $P_{1\alpha}^{-1}P_{1\beta}$ transforms α into β because the first factor changes α into 1 and the second 1 into β. Hence G is transitive.

Since the order of a group is divisible by the index of any of its subgroups (p. 37), we have the

COROLLARY. *The order of a transitive group of permutations of degree* n *is divisible by* n.

The concept of transitiveness may be generalized in the following way.

DEFINITION 4. *A group of permutations is said to be* **k-ply transitive** *if it contains at least one permutation which changes any set of* k *distinct symbols* α_1, α_2, ..., α_k *into any other such set* β_1, β_2, ... β_k (the α's need not be distinct from the β's). *A* k-ply transitive group is a fortiori l-ply transitive, where $l < k$.

The symmetric group P_n is obviously k-ply transitive, where k is any of the integers 1, 2, ..., n.

The number of distinct sets of symbols α_1, α_2, ..., α_k is

$$v = n(n-1) \ldots (n-k+1),$$

regard being had to the order of the symbols in the set. Let H be the subgroup of all permutations of G which leave the set

$$1, 2, 3, \ldots, k$$

unchanged. By arguments which are analogous to those used in the proof of Theorem 11 it can be shown that the index of H relative to G is equal to v, there being one coset corresponding to each of the v sets of k letters. Hence we have the result :

THEOREM 12. *The order of a* k-*ply transitive group of degree* n *is divisible by* $n(n-1) \ldots (n-k+1)$.

Alternatively we might have developed the concept of multiple transitiveness inductively by using as definition what from our point of view is a criterion.

THEOREM 13. *The group* G *is* k-*ply transitive if* (i) G *is simply transitive and* (ii) G_1 *is* (k$-$1)-*ply transitive with regard to the symbols* 2, 3, ..., n. E.g., the group $G \equiv A_4$ on p. 77 is doubly transitive because the group G_1, which consists of the permutations

$$I, \quad (2\ 3\ 4), \quad (2\ 4\ 3),$$

is evidently simply transitive, as its leading symbol (2) is capable of being transformed into each of the remaining symbols (3 and 4).

26. Primitive Groups. Let G be a *transitive* group and suppose that it is possible to arrange the n letters on which it operates in an array of r rows and s columns, where

$$rs = n, \quad r > 1, \quad s > 1, \quad . \quad . \quad . \quad (3.58)$$

thus

$$\left.\begin{array}{l} a_1, a_2, \ldots, a_s \\ b_1, b_2, \ldots, b_s \\ k_1, k_2, \ldots, k_s \end{array}\right\} (r \text{ rows}), \quad . \quad . \quad . \quad (3.59)$$

in such a way that the permutations of G either permute the letters of any one row amongst themselves or else interchange the letters of one row with those of another row (in some order) so that two letters which stand in different rows of (3.59) are never transformed into letters of the same row and *vice versa*. A transitive group which has this property is said to be **imprimitive,** and the rows of (3.59) are called **imprimitive systems.** A group for which no imprimitive systems can be found is said to be **primitive**. It should be noted that this distinction applies to transitive permutation groups only.

Example 1. The group $G = \{(1\ 2\ 3\ 4)\}$ which consists of the permutations

$$I, \quad (1\ 2\ 3\ 4), \quad (1\ 3)(2\ 4), \quad (1\ 4\ 3\ 2)$$

is imprimitive, having the imprimitive system

$$\begin{array}{c} 1\ 3 \\ 2\ 4 \end{array} \Big| ,$$

which, by the four permutations of G, is changed into

$$\begin{array}{c} 1\ 3 \\ 2\ 4 \end{array} \Big| , \quad \begin{array}{c} 2\ 4 \\ 3\ 1 \end{array} \Big| , \quad \begin{array}{c} 3\ 1 \\ 4\ 2 \end{array} \Big| , \quad \begin{array}{c} 4\ 2 \\ 1\ 3 \end{array} \Big|$$

respectively.

Example 2. It is quite possible that one group may possess several sets of imprimitive systems. Thus in the case of the four-group

$$(1), \quad (1\ 2)(3\ 4), \quad (1\ 3)(2\ 4), \quad (1\ 4)(2\ 3)$$

each of the arrays

$$\begin{array}{c} 1\ 2 \\ 3\ 4 \end{array} \Big| , \quad \begin{array}{c} 1\ 3 \\ 2\ 4 \end{array} \Big| , \quad \begin{array}{c} 1\ 4 \\ 2\ 3 \end{array} \Big|$$

can serve as a set of imprimitive systems.

A *doubly-transitive* group is always *primitive*. For if the rows of the array

$$\begin{array}{c} a_1, a_2, \ldots \\ b_1, b_2, \ldots \\ \ldots\ldots\ldots \end{array}$$

were imprimitive systems, the group could not contain a permutation that transforms the pair a_1, a_2 into a_1, b_2, which would be a contradiction to the definition of double transitivity.

In particular, all symmetric groups P_n are primitive.

27. General Remarks about Transformations. Let Γ be an aggregate of objects $x, y, \ldots$ (Their nature need not be further specified at present.) By an **automorphism** of Γ we mean an operation A that associates with every x a *unique* image x^A *which is itself an element of* Γ, in such a way that different elements have different images; we shall use the notation

$$A : x \longrightarrow x^A. \qquad \qquad (3.60)$$

If B be another automorphism, the operation AB is defined as the result of first performing A and then B, thus

$$AB : x \longrightarrow (x^A)^B (= x^{AB}), \qquad (3.61)$$

which lays down the *law of composition* for automorphisms. In general, $AB \neq BA$.

The identical operation I makes every object correspond to itself, thus

$$I : x \longrightarrow x^I (= x).$$

It plays the part of the *unit element* in the set of all automorphisms of Γ.

We shall now show that any set of automorphisms A, B, C, ... *obeys the associative law.* Indeed, by a repeated application of (3.61) we have

$$x^{A(BC)} = (x^A)^{BC} = ((x^A)^B)^C$$

and

$$x^{(AB)C} = (x^{AB})^C = ((x^A)^B)^C,$$

i.e. $$x^{A(BC)} = x^{(AB)C}$$

for all x, and therefore

$$A(BC) = (AB)C.$$

This result allows us to prove by an indirect argument that certain sets of elements or operations satisfy the group postulates, and in particular the associative law. It is only required to show that the elements in question may be regarded as automorphic transformations of a suitable aggregate Γ.

Example 1. If Γ be a finite aggregate of n distinct objects, the set of automorphisms consists of the $n!$ permutations, which therefore form a group (p. 64).

Example 2. Let Γ be the aggregate of all points in $[n]$-space. The linear transformation

$$y_i = a_{i1}x_1 + a_{i2}x_2 + \ldots + a_{in}x_n$$

of non-zero determinant $|a_{ik}|$ may be regarded as an automorphism of Γ in which the point x is transformed into y. The set of all these transformations forms an (infinite) group.

An important (infinite) subgroup consists of all transformations which transform the sphere

$$\Gamma_1: \quad x_1{}^2 + x_2{}^2 + \ldots + x_n{}^2 = 1$$

into itself (*orthogonal transformations*).

Example 3. The functions

$$z, \quad \frac{1}{1-z}, \quad \frac{z-1}{z}, \quad \frac{1}{z}, \quad 1-z, \quad \frac{z}{1-z},$$

where z is a complex variable, may be regarded as a set of automorphisms of the complex plane Γ (including the point ∞) into itself (see p. 14).

In all these examples the associative law has thus been indirectly established.

28. Groups related to Geometrical Configurations.

Suppose we are given a configuration of n points in three-dimensional space, and let us consider rotations about a fixed point O. The set of all rotations which merely permutes the n points of the configuration amongst themselves, forms a group which is isomorphic with a (proper or improper) subgroup of P_n. The order of this group is indicative of the symmetry with which the configuration is endowed. In the absence of any symmetry the group reduces to the identical transformation.

We shall now discuss in more detail some cases of special interest.

(i) **Dihedral Groups.** Consider a plane lamina having the shape of a regular polygon of n vertices, and suppose that the two sides of the lamina are completely alike. (Figure 2 illustrates the case in which $n = 6$.) There are

FIG. 2

$2n$ rotations, including the identical operation, which bring the lamina to coincidence with itself. For we may rotate the lamina through one of the angles

$$0, \ \frac{2\pi}{n}, \ 2.\frac{2\pi}{n}, \ \ldots, \ (n-1)\frac{2\pi}{n}$$

about the line through the centre O and perpendicular to the plane of the lamina. These n operations may be denoted by

$$I, A, A^2, \ldots, A^{n-1},$$

where A represents a rotation through $2\pi/n$ and

$$A^n = I. \qquad . \qquad . \qquad . \qquad (3.62)$$

A further operation consists in reversing the two sides of the lamina. This may be accomplished by a rotation C through π about a line joining the centre to one of the vertices. It must be understood that this line does *not* take part in any rotation but is assumed to retain its

G

orientation in space. To fix the ideas, let us take 01 as the axis of the rotation C. We have

$$C^2 = I, \quad \cdot \quad \cdot \quad \cdot \quad \cdot \quad (3.63)$$

since C^2 corresponds to a rotation through 2π, i.e. 0, and the $2n$ operations

$$C^\lambda A^\mu \quad (\lambda = 0, 1 \; ; \; \mu = 0, 1, \ldots, n-1) \quad \cdot \quad (3.64)$$

represent all possible automorphic transformations of the lamina ; for they allow any vertex to be brought into the position of any other with or without reversal of the two sides of the lamina.

In order to complete the multiplication table we have to find a relation between A and C. A little geometrical consideration shows that

$$AC = CA^{-1}, \quad \cdot \quad \cdot \quad \cdot \quad \cdot \quad (3.65)$$

which in virtue of (3.63) is equivalent to

$$(AC)^2 = I. \quad \cdot \quad \cdot \quad \cdot \quad \cdot \quad (3.66)$$

(The reader is recommended to verify (3.65) by drawing diagrams analogous to those on p. 8.) We remark that the $2n$ elements of the group might equally well have been denoted by

$$A^\mu C^\lambda \quad (\lambda = 0, 1 \; ; \; \mu = 0, 1, \ldots, n-1), \quad \cdot \quad (3.67)$$

which on account of (3.65) is evidently equivalent to (3.64). Our results may be summarized as follows :

The rotations which transform a regular n-gonal lamina into itself, form a group of order $2n$. *It is called the* **dihedral group** *of order* $2n$, *and its defining relations are*

$$A^n = C^2 = (AC)^2 = I. \quad \cdot \quad \cdot \quad \cdot \quad (3.68)$$

It will be recalled that the dihedral groups of orders 6 and 8 were introduced in (2.58) and (2.61) respectively, subject to the associative law being confirmed. This has now been done for all dihedral groups, since they may be represented as groups of rotations.

The dihedral group of order 6 is isomorphic with P_3 (p. 69).

It is of interest to obtain analytical expressions for the operations of the dihedral group of order $2n$. If x be a variable ranging over the values $1, 2, \ldots, n$, which denote the vertices of the lamina in counter-clockwise order, the operation A is described * by the congruence relation

$$x^A \equiv x + 1 \ (\text{mod. } n). \qquad \ldots \qquad (3.69)$$

Again, if $x = 1 + z$, the image of x under the operation C is given by $x^C = 1 - z$. Thus we have

$$x^C \equiv 2 - x \ (\text{mod. } n). \qquad \ldots \qquad (3.70)$$

All relations between the generating elements A and C may be derived from (3.69) and (3.70) ; e.g., we have

$$x^{AC} \equiv x^C + 1 \equiv 2 - x + 1 = 3 - x,$$
$$x^{(AC)^2} \equiv 3 - (3 - x) = x,$$

i.e. $\qquad\qquad\qquad (AC)^2 = I,$

as in (3.66).

(ii) **The Tetrahedral Group.** Consider a regular tetrahedron with vertices $1, 2, 3, 4$ which is free to rotate about its centre O. There are twelve rotations which transform the tetrahedron into itself. For one of the vertices, say 1, can be brought into the position of any of the four vertices $1, 2, 3, 4$, and the solid can then be rotated through one of the angles 0 or $2\pi/3$ or $4\pi/3$ about the line joining this vertex to the centre, whereby the three faces meeting at the vertex are cyclically interchanged. Thus we have 4×3 operations in all.

Each operation of the tetrahedral group permutes the vertices in some way ; it is therefore isomorphic with a subgroup of P_4. If one vertex be fixed, the remaining

* The notation x^A has, of course, nothing to do with that for a power of x.

three vertices α, β, γ can only be permuted cyclically. Hence the tetrahedral group includes all possible cycles (α, β, γ). We have seen on p. 78 that these cycles generate the group A_4, which is also of order 12. Thus the tetrahedral group contains A_4, but as it is of the same order as A_4, it follows that the *tetrahedral group is isomorphic with the alternating group* A_4.

(iii) **The Octahedral (Hexahedral) Group.** The centres of the faces of a regular octahedron may be regarded as the vertices of a cube (hexahedron), and conversely to every cube we can inscribe an octahedron whose vertices lie at the centres of the faces of the cube. Hence the two solids have the same properties of symmetry, i.e. if one is transformed into itself, so is the other. Thus *the octahedral and hexahedral groups are identical*, though only the first name is in common use. In the present discussion of this group we find it more convenient to consider a cube than an octahedron.

First of all, we see that the octahedral group consists of twenty-four operations, because each vertex of the cube may be brought into the position of any of the eight vertices, and when this has been done, the solid may be rotated through one of the angles 0 or $2\pi/3$ or $4\pi/3$ about the diameter through this vertex, giving in all 8×3, i.e. 24, rotations, including the identity.

The four diagonals of the cube are permuted amongst themselves when the cube is transformed into itself. If a diagonal is carried over into itself, it either coincides with the axis of rotation, or else the operation interchanges its two end-points ; in this case the axis of rotation is at right-angles to the diagonal and the angle of rotation is π. We infer that no rotation of the cube can transform each of the four diagonals into itself ; for the axis of such a rotation would have to be at right-angles to at least three diagonals, which is obviously impossible. Hence two distinct rotations of the octahedral group correspond to two distinct permutations of the four diagonals. As there exist only twenty-four permutations of four objects, it follows that *the octahedral group is isomorphic with the symmetric group P_4.*

(iv) **The Icosahedral (Dodecahedral) Group.** Turning now to the last two of the regular polyhedra, we observe that the icosahedron and dodecahedron have the same properties of symmetry. For the centres of the twenty faces of an icosahedron may be joined to form a regular dodecahedron, and conversely, the twelve vertices of an icosahedron can be placed at the centres of the faces of a suitable dodecahedron. Thus *the icosahedral and dodecahedral groups are identical,* and either solid may be used to examine the nature of the group elements. We decide to choose the dodecahedron, with which the reader of this series of University Texts is no doubt more familiar, seeing it, as he does, on the cover of each volume that he takes into his hand.

First of all we remark that the dodecahedral group contains sixty distinct operations. For any vertex may be brought into the position of one of the twenty vertices, and after the vertex has reached its final position, the solid may be rotated about the diameter through it. These operations cause cyclic interchanges of the three faces which meet at the extremities of the diameters. The possible angles of rotation are therefore 0, $2\pi/3$, $4\pi/3$, whence it follows that there are 20×3 ($=60$) distinct rotations (including the identity) which bring the dodecahedron into coincidence with itself.

In Euclid's classical construction * a dodecahedron is derived from a cube in such a way that each of the twelve edges of the cube is a diagonal in one of the faces of the dodecahedron. Conversely, if we start with a given diagonal, we can inscribe in the dodecahedron one, and only one, cube which has this diagonal as one of its edges. Since each face has five diagonals, it follows that five cubes can thus be inscribed. Any rotation of the dodecahedron into itself induces a permutation of the five cubes. Bearing

* Elements, Book XIII, Proposition 17.

in mind that the edges of each cube are in $(1, 1)$-correspondence with the faces of the dodecahedron, the reader will have no difficulty in convincing himself that no rotation of the latter (except the identity) leaves all five cubes in their original position or merely transforms each cube into itself. Hence different rotations give rise to different permutations of the five cubes, i.e. the dodecahedral group is isomorphic with a certain subgroup of order 60 of the symmetric group P_5. As we shall prove in Chapter IV, Corollary 1, p. 123, that the alternating group A_5 is the only subgroup of P_5 of order 60, we can state that the dodecahedron group is isomorphic with A_5.

Examples

(1) Resolve (i) $\begin{pmatrix} 1\,2\,3\,4\,5\,6\,7\,8\,9 \\ 4\,6\,9\,7\,2\,5\,8\,1\,3 \end{pmatrix}$ and (ii) $\begin{pmatrix} a\,b\,c\,d\,e\,f \\ c\,e\,d\,f\,b\,a \end{pmatrix}$ into cycles. Find the orders of the two given permutations.

(2) Express in terms of mutually exclusive cycles

(i) $(abc \ldots k)(al)$;

(ii) $(a_1 a_2 \ldots a_r x y b_1 b_2 \ldots b_s)(a_r a_{r-1} \ldots a_1 x y c_1 c_2 \ldots c_t)$;

(iii) $(a_1 a_2 \ldots a_r x y z b_1 b_2 \ldots b_s)(a_r a_{r-1} \ldots a_1 x y z c_1 c_2 \ldots c_t)$.

(3) Verify that the permutations $(1\ 2)(3\ 4)$ and $(1\ 3)(2\ 4)$ commute.

(4) Show that $(ab \ldots lx)(x\alpha\beta \ldots \lambda) = (ab \ldots l\alpha\beta \ldots \lambda x)$, where $a, b, \ldots, l, x, \alpha, \beta, \ldots, \lambda$ are distinct symbols.

(5) Prove that a cycle of degree m is even or odd according as m is odd or even.

(6) Show that a permutation of degree n which is the product of r cycles (including those of order 1) is even or odd according as $n - r$ is even or odd.

(7) Prove that P_n may be generated by the transpositions

$$(1\ 2), \ (2\ 3), \ \ldots, \ (n-1, \ n).$$

(8) Show that P_n may be generated by the cycle $C = (1\ 2 \ldots n)$ and any transposition $T = (ab)$.

(9) Prove that every regular permutation can be expressed as the power of a cycle and that, conversely, if $C = (1\ 2\ \ldots\ n)$, then C^s is a regular permutation consisting of d cycles of degree m' where $d = (m, s)$ and $m' = m/d$.

(10) Let G_i ($i = 1, 2, \ldots, g$) be the elements of an abstract group G and associate with every element R of G the permutation $\widetilde{R}$ which changes G_i into $R^{-1}G_i$. Prove that (i) the set of all $\widetilde{R}$ forms a group $\overline{\mathsf{G}}$ which is isomorphic with G, (ii) every permutation of $\overline{\mathsf{G}}$ commutes with every element of G' (of Cayley's Theorem, p. 80), (iii) a permutation that commutes with every permutation of $\overline{\mathsf{G}}$ belongs to G', and *vice versa*.

(11) Obtain the group which transforms a rectangular lamina into itself.

(12) Prove that when the g permutations of a transitive group of degree n are written as products of mutually exclusive cycles, they contain between them $(n-1)g$ letters.

HINTS and ANSWERS. 1. (i) $(1\ 4\ 7\ 8)(2\ 6\ 5)(3\ 9)$, (ii) $(a\ c\ d f)$ $(b\ e)$, orders 12, 4. 2. (i) $(abc \ldots kl)$, (ii) $(a_r y b_1 \ldots b_s x c_1 \ldots c_t)$, (iii) $(a_r y c_1 c_2 \ldots c_t)(x z b_1 b_2 \ldots b_s)$. 8. Consider the permutations $C^{-r} T C^r$ where $r = 0, 1, \ldots, n-1$. 10. (iii) Let $G_i \longrightarrow f(G_i)$ be such a permutation ; if it commutes with every element of G', we must have $f(G_i P) = f(G_i) P$ for every P of G. Put $G_i = I$. 11. The four-group. 12. In the expansion of G relative to G_1 the letter 1 occurs in all permutations which do not belong to G_1, i.e. $g - g/n$ times ; the same is true for the other letters.

CHAPTER IV

INVARIANT SUBGROUPS

29. Classes of Conjugate Elements. In this and the following chapter we shall again be concerned with general properties of abstract groups.

DEFINITION 1. *Two elements* A *and* B *of a group* G *are said to be* **conjugate** *with respect to* G *if there exists an element* T *in* G *such that*

$$T^{-1}AT = B. \qquad . \qquad . \qquad . \qquad (4.1)$$

The element T, which need not be unique, is called the **transforming element**. We note that the relation of conjugacy is (i) *reflexive*, i.e. A is conjugate with itself because $I^{-1}AI = A$, (ii) *symmetrical*, i.e. if A is conjugate with B, then B is conjugate with A because (4.1) implies that $T_1^{-1}BT_1 = A$ where $T_1 = T^{-1}$, (iii) *transitive*, i.e. if A is conjugate with B and B is conjugate with C, then A is conjugate with C because if $T^{-1}AT = B$ and $S^{-1}BS = C$ it follows that $(TS)^{-1}A(TS) = C$.

We have already seen (p. 22) that conjugate elements are of the same order.

The complex which consists of all elements conjugate with A (including A itself) is called the **class** of A and will be denoted by (A), thus

$$(A) = A + T_2^{-1}AT_2 + T_3^{-1}AT_3 + \ldots.$$

It is of interest to determine the number of distinct elements in (A). This is best done by enquiring what elements of G commute with A : if N_1 and N_2 be two such elements we have

$$AN_1 = N_1A, \quad AN_2 = N_2A,$$

and therefore

$$A(N_1N_2) = (AN_1)N_2 = (N_1A)N_2 = N_1(AN_2) = (N_1N_2)A,$$

i.e. the product N_1N_2 also commutes with A. Thus *the elements of G which commute with a fixed element* A *form a subgroup* N_A *of order* n_A, *say*; *it is called the* **normalizer** *of* A. For brevity let us put $N = N_A$ and $n = n_A$. Suppose that the expansion of G into cosets relative to N is

$$G = NT_1 + NT_2 + \ldots + NT_h \quad (T_1 = I), \quad . \quad (4.2)$$

where h ($= g/n$) is the index of the normalizer. A typical element of NT_i may be written NT_i, where N is any element of N, i.e. any element which commutes with A. We have

$$(NT_i)^{-1}A(NT_i) = T_i^{-1}(N^{-1}AN)T_i = T_i^{-1}AT_i,$$

irrespective of the element N chosen. Thus all elements which belong to the same coset in (4.2) transform A alike. Conversely, two elements from different cosets transform A differently. For if not, we should have a relation

$$T_i^{-1}AT_i = T_j^{-1}AT_j,$$

whence

$$A(T_iT_j^{-1}) = (T_iT_j^{-1})A,$$

which means that $T_iT_j^{-1}$ commutes with A and therefore belongs to N, i.e. by Chapter II, Lemma 2, p. 34, $NT_i = NT_j$. Thus the index of the normalizer of A is equal to the exact number of distinct conjugates of A. We collect these results in the following statement.

THEOREM 1. *Those elements of G which commute with a given element* A, *form a subgroup* N *of order* n (*the normalizer of* A). *If*

$$G = NT_1 + NT_2 + \ldots + NT_h,$$

where g = nh, *then the class* (A) *contains* h *distinct elements which can be written*

$$T_1^{-1}AT_1, \, T_2^{-1}AT_2, \ldots, T_h^{-1}AT_h. \quad . \quad (4.3)$$

We might paraphrase this important theorem as follows : let A be a fixed element of G and let X run through the g elements of G. Of the g elements $X^{-1}AX$, which are thus formally obtained, only h are distinct, each occurring n times where n is the order and h the index of the normalizer of A $(g = nh)$.

An element A forms a class by itself $(h = 1)$ if, and only if, its normalizer is identical with the whole group $(g = n)$, i.e. A commutes with all elements of G. Such an element is called an **invariant** or **self-conjugate element** of G. In an Abelian group every element is invariant and the concept of classes becomes illusory. In every group, I is an invariant element, i.e.

$$(I) = I,$$

because $X^{-1}IX = I$ for every element X.

The various classes of conjugate elements are *mutually exclusive* ; for if (A) and (B) had an element in common, we should have an equation

$$T^{-1}AT = S^{-1}BS,$$

whence $X^{-1}AX = (ST^{-1}X)^{-1}B(ST^{-1}X)$ for every element X of G. Thus every element of (A) would belong to (B), and by a similar argument we could show that (B) was completely contained in (A). Hence two distinct classes have no element in common. Since each element of G belongs to some class, we have a decomposition of the form

$$G = (A_1) + (A_2) + \ldots + (A_k), \qquad . \qquad . \qquad (4.4)$$

where k is the number of distinct classes. On equating the number of elements on both sides of (4.4) we obtain the important relation

$$g = h_1 + h_2 + \ldots + h_k, \qquad . \qquad . \qquad (4.5)$$

where h_i is the number of elements in (A_i). We repeat that

$$h_i \mid g \quad (i = 1, 2, \ldots, k) \qquad . \qquad . \qquad (4.6)$$

and that $h_i = 1$ if, and only if, A_i is self-conjugate.

The following theorem is a simple application of these results.

THEOREM 2. *If a group is of order* p^m, *where* p *is a prime, the number of its self-conjugate elements is a positive multiple of* p.

Proof. In (4.5) each term, being a factor of p^m, is either equal to unity or else is of the form $p^\mu(\mu > 0)$. If there be z terms of the former type, the group has z self-conjugate elements. Hence after suitable rearrangement (4.5) becomes

$$p^m = z + p^\mu + p^{\mu'} + \ldots \quad (0 < \mu \leqslant \mu' \leqslant \ldots).$$

From this equation it is evident that z must be a multiple of p; and since I is a self-conjugate element and therefore $z \geqslant 1$, it follows that z is in fact a positive multiple of p.

30. Invariant Subgroups. The concept of normalizer is not confined to single elements. If K be a given complex of G, any complex of the form $X^{-1}KX$ is said to be conjugate with K relative to G. Those elements of G which commute with K, i.e. for which

$$N^{-1}KN = K \quad \text{or} \quad KN = NK,$$

form a group N which is called the **normalizer** of K in G. In analogy to Theorem 1 we have

THEOREM 3. *The number of distinct complexes conjugate with* K *is equal to the index of its normalizer.*

A complex which commutes with every element of G $(N = G)$ is said to be **invariant** or **self-conjugate** in G. In particular, if the complex be a subgroup we have

DEFINITION 2. *A subgroup* H *is called an* **invariant** (*or* **normal** *or* **self-conjugate**) *subgroup of* G *if it commutes with every element of* G, *i.e. if*

$$HX = XH \quad \text{or} \quad X^{-1}HX = H \quad . \quad . \quad (4.7)$$

for every element X *of* G.

It should be noted that (4.7) is a relation between *complexes*, i.e. if H be an element of H, the condition of invariance demands that $X^{-1}HX$ should be some element H' of H, which, however, need not be the same as H.

If A be any subgroup of G whatsoever, the groups (see Chapter II, Theorem 2, p. 33)

$$X^{-1}AX, \quad Y^{-1}AY, \quad Z^{-1}AZ, \ldots$$

are called the **conjugate subgroups** of A. Thus *a subgroup is invariant if, and only if, it coincides with all its conjugate subgroups*. The two improper subgroups I and G are invariant subgroups of G.

In an Abelian group all subgroups are invariant. We shall use the symbolical notation

$$H \lessdot G \quad \text{or} \quad G \gtrdot H$$

to express that H is an invariant subgroup of G.

We should like to emphasize once more that the concept of invariance is a relative one, i.e. if $H \lessdot G$ and $H \subset G_1 \subset G \subset G_0$, it must not be taken for granted that H is an invariant subgroup of G_0; on the other hand, we have of course $H \lessdot G_1$.

If H be an invariant subgroup and

$$X = X_1 + X_2 + \ldots + X_m$$

any complex of G, we have $X_i H = H X_i$, whence on summing over i,

$$XH = HX. \quad \ldots \quad \ldots \quad (4.8)$$

Using (4.7) and the rules (2.36) and (2.41) for the H.C.F. and L.C.M., we obtain the following results :

(i) *if $H_1 \lessdot G$, $H_2 \lessdot G$, $\ldots$, then $(H_1, H_2, \ldots) \lessdot G$.*

(ii) *if $K_1, K_2, \ldots$ are invariant complexes, then $\{K_1, K_2, \ldots\}$ is an invariant subgroup.*

The invariant subgroups arrived at under (i) and (ii) might well be improper subgroups.

The following simple fact is frequently used :

THEOREM 4. *A subgroup of index 2 is always an invariant subgroup.*

Proof. Let H be a subgroup of G of index 2 so that there are only two cosets of G relative to H. Thus if S be any element of G that does not belong to H, neither HS nor SH has an element in common with H.   Hence

$$G = H + HS \quad \text{and} \quad G = H + SH.$$

It follows that

$$HS = SH.$$

In addition we have $HH = HH$ for every element H of H (see (2.14), p. 32), and hence also $H(HS) = (HS)H$. Since every element X of G is either of the form H or HS, we infer that $HX = XH$ is universally true, i.e. H is an invariant subgroup.

Example 1.   In the dihedral group

$$D_{2n} : \quad A^n = C^2 = (AC)^2 = I,$$

the cyclic group $A = \{A\}$ of order n is an invariant subgroup of index 2.

Example 2.   The alternating group A_n is an invariant subgroup of P_n.

If A belong to an invariant subgroup H, so does every element of the form $X^{-1}AX$, where X is an arbitrary element of G, i.e. each element of the *class* (A) is contained in H.   *Thus an invariant subgroup is composed of complete classes of* G

$$H = (I) + (A) + (B) + \ldots$$

and conversely, if the sum of several such classes satisfy the group postulates, it constitutes an invariant subgroup of G.

Example 3.   The twenty-four elements of P_4 may be arranged according to classes as follows :

$K_0 = I$

$K_1 = (1 \ 2) + (1 \ 3) + (1 \ 4) + (2 \ 3) + (2 \ 4) + (3 \ 4)$

$K_2 = (1 \ 2 \ 3) + (1 \ 2 \ 4) + (1 \ 3 \ 2) + (1 \ 3 \ 4) + (1 \ 4 \ 2)$
$\qquad\qquad\qquad\qquad\qquad + (1 \ 4 \ 3) + (2 \ 3 \ 4) + (2 \ 4 \ 3)$

$$K_3 = (1\ 2)(3\ 4) + (1\ 3)(2\ 4) + (1\ 4)(2\ 3)$$
$$K_4 = (1\ 2\ 3\ 4) + (1\ 2\ 4\ 3) + (1\ 3\ 2\ 4) + (1\ 3\ 4\ 2)$$
$$+ (1\ 4\ 2\ 3) + (1\ 4\ 3\ 2).$$

It can be verified that the complex

$$V = K_0 + K_3 = I + (1\ 2)(3\ 4) + (1\ 3)(2\ 4) + (1\ 4)(2\ 3) \quad (4.9)$$

forms a group (see p. 82) ; this is therefore an invariant subgroup of P_4.

31. The Quotient (Factor) Group. Let H be an invariant subgroup of G and consider the decomposition

$$G = HS_1 + HS_2 + \ldots + HS_n \quad (S_1 = I), \quad . \quad (4.10)$$

where $g = hn$. Now consider the product $(HS_i)(HS_j)$. Since, by (4.7), $S_i H = HS_i$, we find that

$$(HS_i)(HS_j) = HHS_iS_j = HS_iS_j,$$

using (2.17), p. 33. The last expression is of the form HX and is therefore equal to one of the terms in (4.10), say

$$H(S_iS_j) = HS_k.$$

Thus we have

$$(HS_i)(HS_j) = HS_k. \quad . \quad . \quad . \quad (4.11)$$

This result is of fundamental importance as it allows us to regard the n cosets

$$HS_1, HS_2, \ldots, HS_n \quad (S_1 = I) \quad . \quad . \quad (4.12)$$

as elements of a *group* of order n. Its multiplication table is typified by (4.11) ; the *unit element* of this group is H because

$$H(HS) = H^2S = HS$$

and

$$(HS)H = HHS = HS$$

by (4.7). Any complex HX is equal to one of the cosets (4.12) even if X is not one of the elements S. Thus the *inverse* of HS may be written in the form HS^{-1}, because

$$(HS)(HS^{-1}) = H^2SS^{-1} = H,$$

and we infer that it, too, belongs to the set (4.12), though it may there have been expressed differently. Finally we remark that the *associative law* is fulfilled, having been generally established for complexes in Chapter II ((2.7), p. 30). The group (4.12) is called the **quotient group** of G *relative to* H or the **factor group** *of* H *in* G and is denoted by G/H. Its order is g/h ($=n$).

It should be noted that equation (4.11), which lead to the idea of a quotient group, is essentially based on the invariance of H. The term quotient group and the symbol G/H will not be used unless H is an invariant subgroup of G.

Example. In example 3 on p. 101 the cosets of P_4 relative to the invariant subgroup V can be expressed as follows :

$$V_1 = V = I + (1\ 2)(3\ 4) + (1\ 3)(2\ 4) + (1\ 4)(2\ 3),$$
$$V_2 = V(1\ 2\ 3) = (1\ 2\ 3) + (1\ 3\ 4) + (2\ 4\ 3) + (1\ 4\ 2),$$
$$V_3 = V(1\ 3\ 2) = (1\ 3\ 2) + (2\ 3\ 4) + (1\ 2\ 4) + (1\ 4\ 3),$$
$$V_4 = V(1\ 2) = (1\ 2) + (3\ 4) + (1\ 3\ 2\ 4) + (1\ 4\ 2\ 3),$$
$$V_5 = V(1\ 3) = (1\ 3) + (1\ 2\ 3\ 4) + (2\ 4) + (1\ 4\ 3\ 2),$$
$$V_6 = V(1\ 4) = (1\ 4) + (1\ 2\ 4\ 3) + (1\ 3\ 4\ 2) + (2\ 3).$$

The reader may verify that the six cosets V_i ($i = 1, 2, \ldots, 6$) form a group, namely P_4/V, which is isomorphic with P_3 (see Table 4, p. 15), e.g.,

$$V_2 V_6 = V(1\ 2\ 3)(1\ 4) = V(1\ 2\ 3\ 4) = V(1\ 3) = V_5.$$

32. The Central. The aggregate of self-conjugate elements of G, including I, forms an *Abelian* group Z, which is called the **central** of G. For if A and B are self-conjugate elements, we have $X^{-1}AX = A$ and $X^{-1}BX = B$ for every element X of G, and therefore

$$X^{-1}(AB)X = (X^{-1}AX)(X^{-1}BX) = AB,$$

which proves the group property. Also $B^{-1}AB = A$, i.e.

$$AB = BA.$$

Alternatively, *the central may be defined as the aggregate of those elements of G which commute with all elements of G.* In some groups the central reduces to the single element I, while the opposite extreme occurs in Abelian groups where $Z = G$. The central is, so to speak, the Abelian part of a group.

The central is always an invariant subgroup, because the equation $X^{-1}ZX = Z$ is certainly satisfied, since in fact $X^{-1}ZX = Z$ for each element of Z.

As an application of these ideas we shall prove:

THEOREM 5. *A group of order* p², *where* p *is a prime, is always Abelian.*

Proof. By Theorem 2, the order of the central of a group of order p^2 is either p^2 or p. The former alternative is equivalent to saying that the whole group G is identical with Z and is therefore Abelian. It remains to consider the case in which Z is of order p. The quotient group G/Z is then of order p^2/p, i.e. p, and hence is a cyclic group. Thus we may write

$$G = Z + ZP + \ldots + ZP^{p-1}.$$

Two typical elements of G may be written

$$G_1 = Z_1 P^\lambda, \quad G_2 = Z_2 P^\mu,$$

where Z_1 and Z_2 belong to Z and therefore commute with all elements of G. Hence

$$G_1 G_2 = Z_1 Z_2 P^{\lambda+\mu} = Z_2 Z_1 P^{\lambda+\mu} = G_2 G_1,$$

i.e. G is Abelian.

33. The Commutator Group. Corresponding to any two elements S and T of G, we define a **commutator** U by the equation

$$U = S^{-1} T^{-1} ST. \qquad \qquad (4.13)$$

Evidently $U = I$ if, and only if, $ST = TS$. In an Abelian group all commutators are equal to the unit element.

Suppose that on making S and T run independently through the whole group we obtain the commutators

$$U_1, U_2, \ldots, U_m. \qquad . \qquad . \qquad . \quad (4.14)$$

It is possible that the product of two commutators cannot itself be written as a commutator. But in any case *the set of all commutators generates a certain group*

$$U = \{U_1, U_2, \ldots, U_m\},$$

which is called the **commutator group** *of* G. If $U = G$, the group G is called a **perfect group**.

THEOREM 6. *The commutator group is an invariant subgroup, and its quotient group is Abelian; it is contained in every invariant subgroup which has an Abelian quotient group.*

Proof. (i) If X be any element of G and if U be a typical commutator, we have

$$X^{-1}UX = X^{-1}S^{-1}T^{-1}STX = S_1^{-1}T_1^{-1}S_1T_1,$$

where $S_1 = X^{-1}SX$ and $T_1 = X^{-1}TX$. Hence $X^{-1}UX$ is also a commutator, i.e.

$$X^{-1}UX = U,$$

which proves that U is an invariant subgroup of G.

(ii) The elements of G/U are the complexes UX; the commutator of two such complexes can be written

$$(UX^{-1})(UY^{-1})(UX)(UY) = UX^{-1}Y^{-1}XY, \quad (4.15)$$

in virtue of the multiplication table for the quotient group. Now $X^{-1}Y^{-1}XY$ is itself an element of U and may therefore be absorbed by the factor U on the right-hand side of (4.15). Hence in G/U every commutator is equal to U, which is the unit element of that group, i.e. G/U is Abelian.

(iii) If R be any invariant subgroup of G whose quotient group is Abelian, then by the preceding argument

$$RX^{-1}Y^{-1}XY = R,$$

i.e. R contains $X^{-1}Y^{-1}XY$, which may be any element of U, thus $R \supset U$.

We conclude this section by proving the following result.

THEOREM 7. *If A and B be two invariant subgroups which have only the unit element in common, then every element of A commutes with every element of B.*

Proof. Consider the commutator

$$U = A^{-1}B^{-1}AB = (A^{-1}B^{-1}A)B = A^{-1}(B^{-1}AB),$$

where A and B are typical elements of A and B.

Since A and B are invariant, $A^{-1}B^{-1}A$ is an element of B and $B^{-1}AB$ is an element of A. Thus it appears that U is an element both of A and of B. By hypothesis it must then be equal to I, i.e. A and B commute.

34. Homomorphisms and Isomorphisms. The idea of isomorphism has already been introduced on p. 19. If G and G' are *isomorphic* groups, we shall write

$$G \sim G'.$$

The mapping of G onto G' can be uniquely reversed, i.e. no two elements have the same image. But the typical feature of the mapping is the *conservation of structure*, which is most concisely expressed by

$$(AB)' = A'B' \quad . \quad . \quad . \quad . \quad (4.16)$$

(see p. 19). Any mapping $G \longrightarrow G'$ which satisfies condition (4.16) is called a **homomorphic** mapping (or a **homomorphism**) of G onto G'. This includes cases in which two different elements of G may have the same image in G'. Thus in a homomorphism structure is retained but individuality may be destroyed.[*]

To mention a trivial case, we can map any group G onto the group whose only element is the number 1 ; in fact, if $A \longrightarrow 1, B \longrightarrow 1, C \longrightarrow 1, \ldots$ a relation of the form $AB = C$

---

[*] Some authors use the word *isomorphism* instead of homomorphism and denote by *simple isomorphism* what we call isomorphism. See footnote on p. 19.

is carried over into $1 \times 1 = 1$, which is evidently true. A rather less obvious example is furnished by the alternating character (Chapter III, Theorem 4, p. 74) of a group of permutations, or by the homomorphic correspondence between a square matrix and its determinant in a group of matrices, where the multiplication theorem of determinants, namely

$$| AB | = | A | \, | B |,$$

is the realization of (4.16).

We shall now prove that if H is an invariant subgroup of G, then G is homomorphic with G/H. In fact, if we construct the mapping

$$X \longrightarrow HX, \quad . \quad . \quad . \quad . \quad (4.17)$$

where X is a typical element of G, we see that corresponding to a relation $XY = Z$ we have

$$(HX)(HY) = H^2 XY = HXY = HZ, \quad . \quad . \quad (4.18)$$

which shows that condition (4.16) is fulfilled. It should be observed that, in accordance with our definition (4.17), all elements of G which belong to the same coset relative to H have the same image; for two such elements are of the form $H_1 X$ and $H_2 X$ respectively, where H_1 and H_2 are any elements of H. Hence by (4.17)

$$H_1 X \longrightarrow H H_1 X = HX$$
$$H_2 X \longrightarrow H H_2 X = HX.$$

It is an interesting fact that, in a sense, all homomorphisms are equivalent to those which are generated by suitable invariant subgroups as in (4.17). Suppose we are given a homomorphic mapping $G \longrightarrow G'$ which is typified by

$$X \longrightarrow X'. \quad . \quad . \quad . \quad . \quad (4.19)$$

It is clear that the image of the unit element I of G is the unit element I' of G'; for since $I^2 = I$, the image of I must satisfy the equation $(X')^2 = X'$, which has no solution apart from I'. Again, since $XX^{-1} = I$ is carried over into $X'(X^{-1})' = I'$, we infer that $(X^{-1})' = (X')^{-1}$, i.e.

$$X^{-1} \longrightarrow (X')^{-1}. \qquad . \qquad . \qquad (4.20)$$

If the homomorphism (4.19) is not an isomorphism, I' is the image of several elements of G. *Let*

$$E = I + E_2 + E_3 + \ldots + E_l \qquad . \qquad . \qquad (4.21)$$

be the complex of all elements of G which are mapped on I'. We shall show that E is an invariant subgroup of G. For if E_i and E_j be any two elements of E, we have $E_i \longrightarrow I'$ and $E_j \longrightarrow I'$, whence by (4.16) $E_i E_j \longrightarrow I'I' = I'$, which shows that the complex (4.21) is a subgroup. Next, if E be a typical element of E and X any element of G whatsoever, we find, with the aid of (4.20), that

$$X^{-1}EX \longrightarrow (X')^{-1}I'X' = I'.$$

Hence all elements of the form $X^{-1}EX$ belong to E, i.e. E is an invariant subgroup.

Finally, we shall prove that G/E is isomorphic with G'. Consider the mapping

$$EX \longrightarrow X' \qquad . \qquad . \qquad . \qquad (4.22)$$

between these groups, where X' is the image of X in accordance with the mapping (4.19) of G onto G'. We have already seen that (4.22) leaves all structural relations unaltered. For on putting $H = E$ in (4.18), we have $(EX)(EY) = E(XY)$, which may be interpreted as $X'Y' = (XY)'$. Moreover, distinct elements of G/E have distinct images in G'; indeed, if we had $EX \longrightarrow X'$ and $EY \longrightarrow X'$, our construction of (4.22) would imply that $X \longrightarrow X'$ and $Y \longrightarrow X'$ in the mapping (4.19), whence $XY^{-1} \longrightarrow X'X'^{-1} = I'$; i.e. XY^{-1} would belong to E, and consequently $EX = EY$. Thus the groups G/E and G' are isomorphic, and the mapping (4.19) is not essentially different from

$$X \longrightarrow EX,$$

which is of the type (4.17), being generated by the invariant subgroup E. We may summarize these results as follows:

THEOREM 8. *If H is an invariant subgroup of G, then G is homomorphic with G/H. In any homomorphism $G \longrightarrow G'$, those elements of G which are mapped on the unit element of G' form an invariant subgroup E of G such that G/E is isomorphic with G'.*

35. Automorphisms.   An interesting type of isomorphism occurs when the group of images coincides with the given group G.

DEFINITION 3. *A $(1, 1)$-mapping Φ of a group G onto itself which associates with every element A of G a unique image A_ϕ in G,*

$$\Phi : A \longrightarrow A_\phi$$

is called an **automorphism** *if*

$$(AB)_\phi = A_\phi B_\phi.$$

It follows from the general results of Chapter III, § 27 that the set of automorphisms forms a group.

There are two types of automorphism: if X be a fixed element of G, the mapping

$$\Xi : A \longrightarrow X^{-1}AX (= A_\xi),$$

which evidently satisfies the above condition, is called an **inner** automorphism.   In the case of an Abelian group all inner automorphisms reduce to the identical mapping $(A_\xi = A)$.   An automorphism which is not equivalent to the transformation by a single element is said to be an **outer** automorphism.

E.g., in the four-group $A^2 = B^2 = I$, $AB = BA$, the mapping $I \longrightarrow I$, $A \longrightarrow B$, $B \longrightarrow A$, $AB \longrightarrow BA (= AB)$ is an outer automorphism.

Again, in a cyclic group $\{A\}$ of order m the correspondence

$$A \longrightarrow A^k$$

constitutes an outer automorphism provided k is prime to m.

36. Theorems on Quotient Groups. If H is an invariant subgroup of G, the quotient group G/H consists of all complexes (cosets) HX of which, however, only g/h are distinct (see (4.10), p. 102). If we wish to regard HX as a *single entity*, i.e. as an element of G/H, we shall temporarily employ the notation

$$(HX)$$

in contrast to

$$HX = H_1X + H_2X + \ldots + H_hX,$$

which stands for the *collection* of h elements of G.

The purpose of the following theorems is to examine in more detail the homomorphism between G and G/H established in Theorem 8. The arguments which at first seem somewhat involved are not really difficult, if it is borne in mind that a relation between several complexes of the form HX admits of two interpretations, one involving elements of G/H and the other elements of G. We pass from the former to the latter by omitting brackets.

THEOREM 9. *If* $H \lessdot G$ *and* $H \subset A \subset G$, *then* $A/H \subset G/H$. *Conversely, every subgroup of* G/H *can be written in the form* A/H, *where* $A \subset G$.

Proof. (i) From the assumptions of the theorem it follows that H is automatically an invariant subgroup of G (p. 100), so that the notation A/H is justified. Hence if

$$A = HT_1 + HT_2 + \ldots + HT_r \quad (T_1 = I), \qquad . \ (4.23)$$

where $r = a/h$, the complexes

$$(HT_1), (HT_2), \ldots, (HT_r) . \qquad . \qquad . \ (4.24)$$

form a group, denoted by A/H, which from the very nature of its elements is seen to be a subgroup of G/H.

(ii) Conversely, suppose that the complexes (4.24) are

known to form a subgroup of G/H so that by the Criterion on p. 33 we have

$$\left[\sum_{i=1}^{r} (HT_i)\right]^2 = \sum_{i=1}^{r} (HT_i). \qquad . \qquad . \quad (4.25)$$

Let us now *define* a complex A of G by equation (4.23). When the round brackets are omitted in (4.25) we obtain

$$A^2 = A,$$

which proves that A is in fact a subgroup.

The next theorem deals with the case in which the subgroup A is an invariant subgroup of G.

THEOREM 10. *If $H < G$ and $H < A < G$, then* (i) $A/H < G/H$ *and* (ii) $\dfrac{G/H}{A/H} \sim G/A$. *Conversely, every invariant subgroup of G/H is of the form A/H, where $A < G$.*

Proof. (i) As in the preceding theorem, we put

$$A = \Sigma HT_i, \quad A/H = \Sigma(HT_i), \qquad . \qquad . \quad (4.26)$$

where i runs from 1 to r. Since A is an invariant subgroup of G we have

$$AX = XA$$

for every element X of G, whence by the first equation (4.26)

$$\Sigma HT_i X = \Sigma XHT_i. \qquad . \qquad . \qquad (4.27)$$

On premultiplying this equation by H and remembering that

$$(H^2 T_i X) = (HT_i)(HX),$$

we can turn it into a relation between cosets, namely

$$[\Sigma(HT_i)](HX) = (HX)[\Sigma(HT_i)]. \qquad . \qquad (4.28)$$

This means that A/H (second equation (4.26)) commutes with every element HX of G/H, i.e. A/H is an invariant subgroup of G/H.

(ii) The correspondence

$$HX \longrightarrow AX \qquad . \qquad . \qquad . \qquad . \qquad (4.29)$$

associates a definite element of G/A with every element of G/H. For if $HX = HX_1$ we have $XX_1^{-1} \subset H$ and therefore also $XX_1^{-1} \subset A$, whence $AX = AX_1$. Moreover, (4.29) is a homomorphic mapping because

$$(HX)(HY) = HXY \longrightarrow AXY = (AX)(AY).$$

Next, let us find those elements of G/H which are mapped on the *unit element* of G/A, i.e. on A. If HX be such an element we must have

$$AX = A,$$

i.e. $$X = A,$$

where A is an element of A; conversely, if $A \subset A$, then

$$HA \longrightarrow AA = A.$$

Thus those cosets of G/H which correspond to the unit element of G/A are precisely those which form the group A/H. By Theorem 8 this group is an invariant subgroup of G/H, i.e.

$$A/H \lessdot G/H,$$

and the quotient group of the last two groups is isomorphic with the group of images in the mapping (4.29), thus

$$\frac{G/H}{A/H} \sim G/A.$$

(iii) Conversely, let the cosets

$$(HT_i) \quad (i = 1, 2, \ldots, r \; ; \; T_1 = I)$$

form an invariant subgroup of G/H, i.e. suppose that

$$[\Sigma(HT_i)](HX) = (HX)[\Sigma(HT_i)].$$

By omitting the brackets and reversing the steps that lead from (4.27) to (4.28), we can write this equation in the form

$$AX = XA,$$

where A is now *defined* by (4.26). Thus we see that A is an invariant subgroup of G. This completes the proof of the theorem.

Let us return to the general *Multiplication Theorem* (p. 56) and apply it to *two invariant subgroups* A and B of G. On putting X equal to B and H equal to A in (4.8), we find that

$$AB = BA,$$

whence we infer from the Multiplication Theorem that the complex

$$C = AB$$

is a group. It is, in fact, an invariant (proper or improper) subgroup of G because

$$X^{-1}CX = X^{-1}ABX = (X^{-1}AX)(X^{-1}BX) = AB = C.$$

The intersection of A and B will be denoted by

$$D = (A, B) ;$$

it is an invariant subgroup of G (p. 100), and hence also of A and B.

THEOREM 11.   *Let A and B be invariant subgroups of G. If $C = AB$ and $D = (A, B)$, then*

$$C/A \sim B/D \quad and \quad C/B \sim A/D.$$

Proof.   Among the elements of C are those of the form $AI \ (=A)$ and $IB \ (=B)$, where A and B are any elements of A and B. These groups are therefore subgroups of C and, being invariant in G, are a fortiori invariant in C (p. 100).

We saw on p. 56 (equations (2.66) and (2.68)) that if the decomposition of B relative to D be expressed in the form

$$B = DB_1 + DB_2 + \ldots + DB_n, \qquad . \qquad (4.30)$$

that of $AB \ (=C)$ relative to A may be written

$$C = AB_1 + AB_2 + \ldots + AB_n. \qquad . \qquad (4.31)$$

In our present case the terms in (4.30) and (4.31) are the elements of B/D and C/A respectively. These groups are therefore of the same order. We shall prove that they are, in fact, isomorphic by showing that the (1, 1)-correspondence

$$AB_i \longleftrightarrow DB_i \quad (i = 1, 2, \ldots, n)$$

represents a homomorphic mapping. For let $(DB_i)(DB_j) = DB_k$ be a typical relation between the elements of B/D. On multiplying by A^2 and remembering that $AD = A$ (Corollary, p. 32), we obtain $(AB_i)(AB_j) = AB_k$, which is the corresponding relation in C/A. Hence $B/D = C/A$. Similarly, it can be proved that $A/D \sim C/B$.

37. The Jordan–Hölder Composition Theorem. It is common practice in mathematics to study complex entities by resolving them into simpler components which in some sense are themselves irreducible. Thus integers are decomposed into primes, polynomials are split up into irreducible factors relative to a given field, and so on. But such a resolution is not of great value unless it possesses the property of *uniqueness* in a well-defined manner.

There are several methods of reducing groups. However, we must confine ourselves to one particular line of approach which is due to C. Jordan and was subsequently elaborated by O. Hölder.

DEFINITION 4. *A group which possesses no proper invariant subgroup is called a* **simple** *group*.

The (cyclic) groups of prime order afford trivial instances of simple groups, as they have no proper subgroups at all (Corollary 2, p. 38). Simple groups of composite order are rather rare and command special interest (see Theorem 13, p. 121).

DEFINITION 5. *A subgroup A is called a* **maximum invariant subgroup** *of G if there exists no invariant subgroup H other than G or A such that*

$$G > H > A. \quad . \quad . \quad . \quad . \quad (4.32)$$

By Theorem 10, (4.32) is equivalent to the statement that G/A has a proper invariant subgroup H/A. Hence we have the following result.

CRITERION. *The subgroup A is a maximum invariant subgroup of G if, and only if, G/A is a simple group.*

A group may well possess several maximum invariant subgroups differing both in structure and order.

If G/A be of prime order, then A is a maximum invariant subgroup.

If G is *not* a simple group, it has a proper invariant subgroup and therefore also a maximum invariant subgroup A, say. Thus

$$G \succ A \succ I. \quad . \quad . \quad . \quad (4.33)$$

It may happen that A is a simple group; if not, we have

$$A \succ A_1,$$

where A_1 is a maximum invariant subgroup of A. Continuing in this way, we arrive at the result that *every group G whatever possesses a* **composition series**, *i.e. a series of subgroups*

$$G \succ A \succ A_1 \succ \ldots \succ A_{r-1} \succ A_r \succ I, \quad . \quad . \quad (4.34)$$

where

$$G/A, \quad A/A_1, \ldots, A_{r-1}/A_r, \quad A_r \quad . \quad . \quad (4.35)$$

are simple groups, which we shall call **composition-quotient-groups**. It should be clearly understood that while A_i is a (maximum) invariant subgroup of A_{i-1}, it need not be invariant with respect to $G, A_1, A_2, \ldots, A_{i-2}$.

If the orders of the groups (4.34) be

$$g, a, a_1, \ldots, a_{r-1}, a_r, \quad . \quad . \quad (4.36)$$

the orders of the quotient groups are

$$g/a, a/a_1, \ldots, a_{r-1}/a_r, a_r . \quad . \quad (4.37)$$

respectively. These integers are known as the **composition indices**. Notice that their product is equal to g.

The following fundamental theorem deals with the uniqueness property of composition series referred to at the beginning of this section.

THEOREM 12 (Jordan-Hölder). *In any two composition series for a group G the composition-quotient-groups are, apart from their sequence, isomorphic in pairs.*

Let us consider in more detail what this theorem implies : suppose that

$$G \succ A \succ A_1 \succ \ldots \succ A_r \succ I \, . \quad . \quad . \quad \text{(I)}$$

and

$$G \succ B \succ B_1 \succ \ldots \succ B_s \succ I \, . \quad . \quad . \quad \text{(II)}$$

are two composition series for G. It is then asserted that the quotient groups

$$G/A, \ A/A_1, \ \ldots, \ A_{r-1}/A_r, \ A_r \quad . \quad . \quad \text{(III)}$$

and

$$G/B, \ B/B_1, \ \ldots, \ B_{s-1}/B_s, \ B_s \quad . \quad . \quad \text{(IV)}$$

are isomorphic in pairs. In particular, it would follow that $r = s$, and that the composition indices

$$g/a, \ a/a_1, \ \ldots, \ a_{r-1}/a_r, \ a_r$$

are, possibly after rearrangement, identical with

$$g/b, \ b/b_1, \ \ldots, \ b_{s-1}/b_s, \ b_s.$$

It was this last fact which was discovered by Jordan, while Hölder later observed that the quotient groups were not only of the same order but actually isomorphic.

Proof. Since the only group of order 2, namely the cyclic group C_2, is simple and possesses the *unique* composition series

$$C_2 \succ I,$$

we have a basis for induction, and we shall henceforth assume that the theorem has already been proved for groups of order less than g.

Let us now return to the given composition series (I) and (II). We have to distinguish two cases :

(i) $A = B$. In this case the series (III) and (IV) become

$$G/A, \quad A/A_1, \ldots, A_{r-1}/A_r, A_r \qquad . \qquad . \qquad \text{(V)}$$

and

$$G/A, \quad A/B_1, \ldots, B_{s-1}/B_s, B_s \qquad . \qquad . \qquad \text{(VI)}$$

respectively. Since we assume that the theorem holds for A, the quotient groups on the right of the vertical line are isomorphic in pairs as they represent composition series for A. In particular we have $r = s$, and since the leading terms of the two series are not only isomorphic, but actually identical, we conclude that the complete series are equivalent in the sense of the theorem.

(ii) $A \neq B$. We have seen that

$$C = AB$$

is an invariant subgroup of G which in turn contains A as an invariant subgroup (p. 113), thus

$$G \succ C \succ A.$$

But since A is a maximum invariant subgroup of G, we must have either $C = A$ or $C = G$. The former alternative must be rejected because B and consequently AB differs from A. Hence we conclude that

$$G = C = AB.$$

Putting $D = (A, B)$ as in Theorem 11, we have

$$G/A \sim B/D \quad \text{and} \quad G/B \sim A/D. \qquad . \qquad (4.38)$$

Since by the Criterion on p. 115 G/A and G/B are simple groups, so are B/D and A/D, i.e. D *is a maximum invariant subgroup both of B and of A*. Let

$$D \succ D_1 \succ \ldots \succ D_t \succ I$$

be any composition series for D whatsoever and consider the following composition series for G :

$$G \succ A \succ D \succ D_1 \succ \ldots \succ D_t \succ I \qquad . \qquad \text{(VII)}$$

and

$$G \succ B \succ D \succ D_1 \succ \ldots \succ D_t \succ I \qquad . \qquad \text{(VIII)}$$

having the quotient groups

$$G/A, A/D \mid, D/D_1, \ldots, D_t$$

and

$$G/B, B/D \mid, D/D_1, \ldots, D_t$$

respectively. The groups on the right of the division line are identical in the two series, while those on the left are isomorphic when arranged crosswise in pairs, as stated in (4.38). Let us write

$$(\text{VII}) \sim (\text{VIII}) \quad . \quad . \quad . \quad . \quad (4.39)$$

to express that these two series have the property demanded by the theorem. Since they have the first two terms in common with (I) and (II) respectively, we may appeal to the hypothesis of induction and state that

$$(\text{I}) \sim (\text{VII}) \quad \text{and} \quad (\text{II}) \sim (\text{VIII}).$$

Combining these results with (4.39), we deduce that $(\text{I}) \sim (\text{II})$. This completes the proof of the Jordan-Hölder theorem.

Example 1. *The alternating group* A_n *is a maximum invariant subgroup of* P_n. We have already seen (p. 101) that $P_n \succ A_n$. Since P_n/A_n is of order 2, it follows from the Criterion on p. 115 that A_n is a maximum invariant subgroup of P_n. Let us find a composition series in the cases where n is equal to 3 or 4.

(i) $n = 3$. A composition series for P_3 can evidently be written

$$P_3 \succ A_3 \succ I, \quad . \quad . \quad . \quad . \quad (4.40)$$

the composition quotient groups being the simple groups

$$P_3/A_3, A_3 \quad . \quad . \quad . \quad . \quad (4.41)$$

of prime orders (composition indices)

$$2, 3 \quad . \quad . \quad . \quad . \quad . \quad (4.42)$$

respectively.

(ii) $n = 4$. The group

$$V: I, (1\ 2)(3\ 4), (1\ 3)(2\ 4), (1\ 4)(2\ 3) \quad . \quad (4.43)$$

is an invariant subgroup of P_4 (example on p. 102). As it consists of even permutations, it is an invariant subgroup of A_4. Again, every element of V, other than I, generates a subgroup of V which is of index 2, and is therefore invariant with respect to V. Hence

$$P_4 \succ A_4 \succ V \succ \{(1\ 2)(3\ 4)\} \succ I \quad . \quad . \quad (4.44)$$

is a composition series for P_4 with composition indices

$$2, 3, 2, 2. \quad . \quad . \quad . \quad (4.45)$$

Example 2. The cyclic group C_6 which is generated by an element A, where $A^6 = I$, possesses a composition series of the form

$$C_6 \succ \{A^2\} \succ I. \quad . \quad . \quad . \quad (4.46)$$

The middle term is a cyclic group of order 3, and the quotient groups of (4.46) are cyclic groups of orders 2 and 3 respectively.

We observe that the quotient groups of (4.40) and (4.46) are isomorphic. Thus we learn that a knowledge of the composition-quotient-groups does not suffice for a reconstruction of the whole group.

DEFINITION 6. *A group G is said to be* **soluble** *if all its composition indices are prime.*

E.g., we see from (4.42) and (4.45) that the groups P_3 and P_4 are soluble.

The decision regarding solubility is often facilitated by the following statement.

CRITERION. *A group G is soluble if it contains an invariant subgroup H such that H and G/H are soluble.*

Proof. If these conditions are fulfilled we have

$$H \succ H_1 \succ \ldots \succ H_r \succ I \quad . \quad . \quad (4.47)$$

and

$$G/H \succ G_1/H \succ \ldots \succ G_s/H \succ H, \quad . \quad (4.48)$$

where all composition indices in (4.47) and (4.48) are prime. (It should be remembered that any subgroup of

G/H can be written in the form A/H and that its unit element is H.) Since by Theorem 10

$$\frac{G_{i-1}/H}{G_i/H} \sim G_{i-1}/G_i \quad (G_0 = G),$$

we infer that

$$G \succ G_1 \succ \ldots \succ G_s \succ H \succ H_1 \succ \ldots \succ H_r \succ I$$

is a composition series for G in which all indices are prime. Hence G is soluble.

38. Galois' Theorem on the Alternating Group. We shall prove in this section that, provided $n > 4$, the alternating group A_n contains no proper invariant subgroup. This is equivalent to saying that any invariant subgroup of A_n which does not merely consist of the unit element is equal to A_n. We begin by proving the following lemma.

LEMMA 1. *If an invariant subgroup H of A_n ($n \geqslant 3$) contains one cycle of degree 3, then $H = A_n$.*

Proof. There is no loss of generality in denoting the cycle in question by (1 2 3). When $n = 3$, the alternating group is generated by (1 2 3), and we have nothing further to prove.

Suppose now that $n > 3$. Since H is an invariant subgroup of A_n it contains every permutation of the form

$$S^{-1}(1\ 2\ 3)S,$$

where S is any *even* permutation whatsoever. In particular, if

$$S = (3\ 2\ k),$$

where k is an integer greater than 3, we find that H contains the permutation

$$(3\ 2\ k)^{-1}(1\ 2\ 3)(3\ 2\ k) = (1\ k\ 2)$$

and consequently also its square, namely

$$(1\ 2\ k), \quad (k = 3, 4, \ldots).$$

By Chapter III, Theorem 9 (p. 78) these special cycles generate the alternating group, i.e. $H = A_n$.

We are now in a position to establish the celebrated result referred to in the heading of this section.

THEOREM 13.   *When* $n > 4$, A_n *is a simple group.*

Proof.   Suppose that H is an invariant subgroup of A_n.

(i) Let H include an element of the form

$$H = ABC \ldots, \quad . \qquad . \qquad . \qquad (4.49)$$

where A, B, C, ... are mutually exclusive cycles and

$$A = (a_1 a_2 a_3 a_4 \ldots a_m) \quad \text{and} \quad m > 3.$$

The permutation

$$S = (a_1 a_2 a_3)$$

commutes with all cycles of (4.49) except the first.   Since S is even, H also contains the permutations

$$H_1 = S^{-1}HS = (S^{-1}AS)BC \ldots$$

and

$$\begin{aligned} H_1 H^{-1} &= (S^{-1}AS)A^{-1} \\ &= (a_2 a_3 a_1 a_4 \ldots a_m)(a_m a_{m-1} \ldots a_4 a_3 a_2 a_1) \\ &= (a_1 a_3 a_m)(a_2)(a_4) \ldots (a_{m-1}) = (a_1 a_3 a_m) \end{aligned}$$

(see (3.19), p. 71).   Hence we infer from the Lemma that $H = A_n$.   From now on we can confine ourselves to cases in which the permutations of H are products of cycles of degrees 2 or 3 only.

(ii) Let H be a permutation of H involving at least two cycles of degree 3.   There is no loss of generality in writing

$$H = (1 \ 2 \ 3)(4 \ 5 \ 6)P,$$

where P does not depend on the first six letters.   Choosing

$$S = (2 \ 3 \ 4)$$

as a transforming element and noting that $S^{-1}PS = P$, we deduce that H must also contain the permutations

$$H_1 = S^{-1}HS = (1\ \ 3\ \ 4)(2\ \ 5\ \ 6)P$$

and

$$H_1H^{-1} = (1\ \ 3\ \ 4)(2\ \ 5\ \ 6)(3\ \ 2\ \ 1)(6\ \ 5\ \ 4) = (1\ \ 2\ \ 4\ \ 3\ \ 6),$$

contradicting our assumption that no cycles of degree greater than 3 should occur.

(iii) Next consider the case in which H involves only one cycle of degree 3, say

$$H = (1\ \ 2\ \ 3)P,$$

where P is a product of mutually exclusive cycles of degree 2 so that $P^2 = I$. We conclude that H contains the permutation

$$H^2 = (1\ \ 2\ \ 3)^2P^2 = (1\ \ 3\ \ 2)$$

and therefore, according to the Lemma, coincides with A_n.

(iv) There remains the possibility that H involves no cycles of degree 3, but is a product of transpositions. Such a case does actually occur when $n = 4$ and leads to the four-group V which we discussed on p. 118. On the other hand, when $n > 4$, we can argue as follows : suppose that

$$H = (1\ \ 2)(3\ \ 4)P$$

is an element of H, where P is independent of the letters 1, 2, 3, 4. If we let

$$S = (2\ \ 3\ \ 4)$$

be a transforming element, we find that H contains the permutations

$$H_1 = S^{-1}HS = (1\ \ 3)(4\ \ 2)P$$

and

$$H_2 = H_1H^{-1} = (1\ \ 3)(4\ \ 2)(1\ \ 2)(3\ \ 4) = (1\ \ 4)(2\ \ 3).$$

Again, on taking

$$T = (1\ \ 4\ \ 5)$$

we conclude that the permutations

$$H_3 = T^{-1}H_2T = (4\ 5)(2\ 3)$$

and

$$H_3H_2{}^{-1} = (4\ 5)(2\ 3)(1\ 4)(2\ 3) = (4\ 5)(1\ 4) = (1\ 4\ 5)$$

also belong to H. Thus it appears that H contains a cycle of degree 3, whence it follows that $H = A_n$. This completes the proof of the theorem.

COROLLARY 1. A_n *is the only subgroup of order $\frac{1}{2}n!$ contained in* P_n.

Proof. Any subgroup H of that order is necessarily an invariant subgroup of P_n (Theorem 4, p. 101). Hence the intersection $D = (A_n, H)$ is an invariant subgroup of A_n. It follows from the above theorem that either $D = I$ or $D = A_n$. If $n > 1$, H contains more than one even permutation and hence has more than one element in common with A_n (Theorem 8, p. 77). Thus $A_n = (A_n, H)$, whence $A_n \subset H$. But, as both groups are of the same order, we have in fact $A_n = H$.

COROLLARY 2. P_n *is not soluble when* $n > 4$. For since A_n is simple when $n > 4$,

$$P_n \succ A_n \succ I$$

is a composition series for P_n. Its composition indices are

$$2, \tfrac{1}{2}n!,$$

the second of which is certainly not prime when $n > 4$.

The concept of soluble groups admits of a very remarkable application in the theory of *algebraical equations*, where it is proved that the general equation of the nth degree can be solved in terms of *radicals* if, and only if, the group P_n is soluble. We have learned that this condition is fulfilled only when $n = 1$, 2, 3, 4, which explains why there are algebraical " formulae " for solving equations whose degree does not exceed 4. On the other hand, we are lead to the conclusion that no such formulae can possibly exist for the quintic or equations of still higher degree.

Examples

(1) By using Theorem 1 (p. 97) or otherwise, prove that the only permutations of P_n which commute with a given cycle of degree n are the powers of that cycle.

(2) Show that when n is odd the cycles on n letters form two classes of conjugate elements relative to A_n, each containing $\frac{1}{2}(n-1)!$ members, and that when n is even the cycles on $(n-1)$ letters are divided into two classes in A_n of $\frac{1}{2}n(n-2)!$ elements each.

(3) Two classes (A) and (A^{-1}), which are generated by inverse elements, are called *inverse* classes. Prove that (i) inverse classes contain the same number of elements and (ii) a group of even order includes at least one class which is identical with its inverse class.

(4) Resolve A_4 into classes of conjugate elements.

(5) Show that if $G = G_1 + G_2 + \ldots + G_g$, the group $\{G_1{}^r, G_2{}^r, \ldots, G_g{}^r\}$ is a (proper or improper) invariant subgroup of G.

(6) Let H be an invariant subgroup of index n in G. If R be an element of G such that R^t is the least positive power of R to lie in H, prove that t is a factor both of n and of the order of R.

(7) Prove that the group $A^4 = B^3 = (AB)^2 = I$ is isomorphic with P_4. Hence or otherwise show that $I + A^2 + B^2A^2B + BA^2B^2$ is an invariant subgroup.

(8) If the commutator C of A and B commutes with both A and B, prove that $(AB)^e = B^e A^e C^{\frac{1}{2}e(e+1)}$.

(9) If each element of a group commutes with every conjugate, show that the commutator of any two elements commutes with both, and prove that the elements whose orders divide a given odd number e, form an invariant subgroup.

(10) Prove that A_4 possesses no subgroup of order 6.

(11) Prove that the commutator group of P_n is A_n.

(12) Find the central of the quaternion group (Table 12, p. 55), and construct the quotient group relative to the central. Also obtain a composition series for the quaternion group.

(13) Do the same for the dihedral group of order 8 (Table 11, p. 55).

HINTS and ANSWERS. 2. The normalizers in A_n of such

cycles are of orders n and $n-1$ respectively. 4. I, $(1\ 2\ 3)+$ $(1\ 4\ 2)+(1\ 3\ 4)+(2\ 4\ 3)$, $(1\ 3\ 2)+(1\ 2\ 4)+(1\ 4\ 3)+(2\ 3\ 4)$, $(1\ 2)(3\ 4)+(1\ 3)(2\ 4)+(1\ 4)(2\ 3)$. 7. Let $A \longrightarrow (1\ 2\ 3\ 4)$, $B \longrightarrow (1\ 3\ 2)$. 10. Such a subgroup would have to be invariant, which is incompatible with the result of Example 4. 11. Consider the commutator of $(1\ 2)$ and $(3\ 4)$. 12. $I+A^2$; isomorphic with V; G, $\{A^4\}$, $\{A^2\}$, I. 13. The same.

CHAPTER V

SYLOW GROUPS AND PRIME POWER GROUPS

39. A Lemma on Abelian Groups. If G be a group of order g, the order of any subgroup of G is a factor of g (Lagrange's Theorem, p. 34). The question whether, conversely, G possesses at least one subgroup whose order is equal to a preassigned factor of g presents great difficulties, which have not yet been surmounted. To be sure, the case of cyclic groups is straightforward, and the answer is in the affirmative, as we saw in Chapter II, Theorem 4, p. 38. But where non-commutative groups are concerned, our knowledge is much more scanty.

We begin by proving a lemma which is a particular case of a theorem of A. Cauchy (see p. 129 below).

LEMMA 1. *If A be an Abelian group of order a and if p be any prime factor of a, then A contains at least one element of order p.*

Proof. The proposition is obviously true when $a = p$ (a prime number). We may therefore employ mathematical induction and shall henceforth assume that a is a composite number divisible by p. By Chapter II, Theorem 5, p. 40 A possesses proper subgroups. Let us select a *proper subgroup H of maximum order* h, $(h < a)$ say. We have to distinguish two cases :

(i) $p \mid h$. By induction, H contains an element $P (\neq I)$ such that $P^p = I$. Since P also belongs to A, this element satisfies our demands.

(ii) $(h, p) = 1$. Since H is a proper subgroup of A, there exists an element T of order t, say, which does not belong to H. Let $T(= \{T\})$ be the cyclic group generated by T and

126

consider the product HT. Since A is Abelian, $HT = TH$ whence, by the Multiplication Theorem (p. 56), it follows that HT is a subgroup of A. It is obviously more comprehensive than H which, on the other hand, was supposed to be a maximal proper subgroup. Hence we must conclude that

$$A = HT.$$

The product on the right-hand side includes ht/d elements, where d is the order of (H, T). Thus we obtain the relation

$$ad = ht.$$

The left-hand side is divisible by p. But since $(p, h) = 1$, it follows that $p \mid t$, i.e.

$$t = ps.$$

The element

$$P = T^s$$

is therefore of order p, as required.

40. Sylow's Theorems. Some remarkable results concerning subgroups of a certain type were discovered by the Norwegian mathematician L. Sylow.*

DEFINITION 1. *If the order of a group G be divisible by* p^m *but by no higher power of* p, *where* p *is a prime, then any subgroup of G of order* p^m *is called a* **Sylow group** *corresponding to* p.

THEOREM 1. *Every group of order g possesses at least one Sylow group corresponding to each prime factor of g.*

Proof. We shall again proceed by mathematical induction. The truth of the theorem is evident when $g = 2$ (the subgroup referred to need not be a proper subgroup). Let $g = p^m g'$, where $(g', p) = 1$. Resolving G into classes of conjugate elements (equation (4.4), p. 98), we have

$$G = (A_1) + (A_2) + \ldots + (A_k),$$

* " Théorèmes sur les groupes de substitutions ", *Math. Ann.* v (1872), p. 584.

and consequently

$$g = h_1 + h_2 + \ldots + h_k, \qquad . \quad . \quad . \quad (5.1)$$

where h_i is the number of elements in the class (A_i). It will be recalled that the normalizer of A_i is a group N_i whose order is given by

$$n_i = g/h_i \quad (i = 1, 2, \ldots, k) \qquad . \quad . \quad (5.2)$$

(Chapter IV, Theorem 1, p. 97). We have to distinguish two cases :

(i) Suppose there exists an integer l between 1 and k such that $h_l > 1$ and $(h_l, p) = 1$. It follows from (5.2) that n_l is *less* than g and is divisible by p^m (but by no higher power of p). Hence, by hypothesis, the theorem is true for N_l and we conclude that N_l possesses a subgroup of order p^m, which is of course also a subgroup of G and therefore a Sylow group corresponding to p.

(ii) Having disposed of case (i), we now assume that for every value of the suffix i in (5.1)

either (a) $h_i = 1$, or (b) $p \mid h_i$.

Terms of the type (a) correspond to self-conjugate elements, and we note that there is at least one such term, since I is a self-conjugate element. Denoting the exact number of self-conjugate elements (i.e. the order of the central) by z (> 0) and collecting in (5.1) all terms which are equal to 1, we obtain

$$p^m g' = z + xp,$$

whence

$$p \mid z.$$

Thus we see that the order of the central is divisible by p. Since it is an Abelian group we learn from the lemma that G possesses at least one element P which commutes with all elements and is of order p, i.e. $X^{-1}PX = P$. The cyclic group

$$P = \{P\}$$

is therefore an invariant subgroup of G and G/P is of order

$p^{m-1}g'$. Hence, by the hypothesis of induction, G/P contains a Sylow group of order p^{m-1}. Such a subgroup can be written in the form H/P where H is a subgroup of G (Chapter IV, Theorem 9, p. 110) of order h, say. Thus we have

$$p^{m-1} = h/p,$$

i.e.

$$h = p^m.$$

The group H arrived at in this way is therefore a Sylow group of G corresponding to p.

As a corollary of this fundamental result we shall deduce Cauchy's theorem referred to at the beginning of this chapter.

THEOREM 2 (Cauchy). *If* p *be a prime factor of the order of a group* G, *then* G *contains at least one element of order* p.

Proof. Let H be a Sylow group of G of order p^m. If H be an element of H other than I, the order of H is of the form p^μ, where $\mu > 0$. Thus if we put

$$P = H^{p^{\mu-1}},$$

we have discovered an element of order p, since

$$P^p = H^{p^\mu} = I, \quad P \neq I.$$

It is quite possible that G may have more than one Sylow group of order p^m. Indeed, if A be one subgroup of this order, so is $X^{-1}AX$, where X is any element of G whatsoever (Chapter II, Theorem 2, p. 33), i.e. all groups conjugate with A are likewise Sylow groups. It might of course happen that some or all of these groups are identical with A. On the other hand, it will now be shown that we need not look for Sylow groups elsewhere.

THEOREM 3. *All Sylow groups belonging to the same prime are conjugate to one another.*

Proof. Let A and B be two subgroups of G of order p^m.

Decomposing G relative to A and B (equation (2.73), p. 59), we have
$$G = AP_1B + AP_2B + \ldots + AP_rB$$
and
$$g = \frac{ab}{d_1} + \frac{ab}{d_2} + \ldots + \frac{ab}{d_r}, \qquad (5.3)$$

where d_ρ is the order of
$$D_\rho = (P_\rho^{-1}AP_\rho, B). \qquad (5.4)$$

In the present case $a = b = p^m$ and $g = p^m g'$, where $(g', p) = 1$. Hence, on dividing (5.3) throughout by p^m, we obtain
$$g' = \frac{p^m}{d_1} + \frac{p^m}{d_2} + \ldots + \frac{p^m}{d_r}. \qquad (5.5)$$

Since D_ρ is a subgroup of B, its order, d_ρ, must be of the form p^μ $(0 \leqslant \mu \leqslant m)$, so that p^m/d_ρ is either a multiple of p, or else equal to unity. However, as the left-hand side of (5.5) is prime to p, not all terms on the right can be multiples of p, i.e. there exists at least one term, when $\rho = l$, say, such that
$$p^m/d_l = 1, \quad \text{i.e. } d_l = p^m.$$

Hence the corresponding group D_l is of the same order as B and since, by (5.4), it is contained in B, it follows that, in fact, $D_l = B$ and, for the same reason, $D_l = P_l^{-1}AP_l$. Hence
$$B = P_l^{-1}AP_l,$$

i.e. the two Sylow groups A and B are conjugate.

An interesting case arises when the Sylow group A is invariant in G, i.e. when it coincides with all its conjugate groups :

COROLLARY. *The Sylow group A is unique if, and only if, it is an invariant subgroup of G.*

A more precise statement regarding the number of Sylow groups is contained in the following :

THEOREM 4. *If there be exactly* k *Sylow groups of* G

corresponding to a prime p, *then* k *is an integer of the form* $1 + px$ *and is a factor of the order of* G.

Proof. Theorem 3 implies that the number of distinct Sylow groups is equal to the number k of distinct groups conjugate with one of them. Let A be a fixed Sylow group corresponding to p and let N be the normalizer of A, i.e. the set of all elements N of G such that

$$N^{-1}AN = A. \quad . \quad . \quad . \quad . \quad (5.6)$$

If N be of order n, we have

$$g = nk . \quad . \quad . \quad . \quad . \quad (5.7)$$

(Chapter IV, Theorem 3, p. 99), which shows that k is a factor of g. Since A is a group, each element A of A satisfies the relation

$$A^{-1}AA = A$$

(Chapter II, Lemma 1, p. 32). Hence A belongs to N ; and, moreover, we infer from (5.6) that A is an invariant subgroup of N, i.e.

$$A \lessdot N. \quad . \quad . \quad . \quad (5.8)$$

Hence p^m, which is the order of A, is a factor of n so that we may write

$$n = p^m n', \quad (n', p) = 1.$$

The last statement is justified because n, being a factor of g, cannot be divisible by a power of p greater than p^m.

Let us now apply Frobenius' identity (Chapter II, Theorem 8, p. 60) to the subgroups A and N of orders p^m and n respectively, thus

$$G = AP_1N + AP_2N + \ldots + AP_rN \quad . \quad . \quad (5.9)$$

and

$$g = \frac{np^m}{d_1} + \frac{np^m}{d_2} + \ldots + \frac{np^m}{d_r}, \quad . \quad . \quad (5.10)$$

where d_ρ is the order of

$$D_\rho = (P_\rho^{-1}AP_\rho', N). \quad . \quad . \quad . \quad (5.11)$$

There is no loss of generality in assuming that $P_1 = I$ and therefore

$$AP_1N = AIN = AN = N.$$

using (5.8) and the corollary on p. 32. The corresponding term in (5.9) is

$$\frac{np^m}{d_1} = n.$$

No other term in the expansion (5.9) is equal to N.

On dividing (5.10) throughout by n after substituting for g from (5.7), we get

$$k = 1 + \frac{p^m}{d_2} + \frac{p^m}{d_3} + \ldots + \frac{p^m}{d_r}. \qquad . \qquad . \qquad (5.12)$$

Now D_ρ is a subgroup of $P_\rho^{-1}AP_\rho$ which, like A, is of order p^m. Hence it follows that p^m/d_ρ is of the form p^μ where $0 \leqslant \mu \leqslant m$. The essential step in the proof is to show that, except in the first term, μ is greater than 0, so that

$$k = 1 + xp. \qquad . \qquad . \qquad . \qquad (5.13)$$

In order to arrive at this result, let us suppose that the λth term in (5.12) reduces to unity, i.e.

$$p^m = d_\lambda. \qquad . \qquad . \qquad . \qquad (5.14)$$

By the same arguments as those which we used in the proof of Theorem 3 (p. 129), we come to the conclusion that $D_\lambda = P_\lambda^{-1}AP_\lambda$, i.e., since D_λ is a subgroup of N,

$$P_\lambda^{-1}AP_\lambda \subset N. \qquad . \qquad . \qquad . \qquad (5.15)$$

We have seen that p^m is the highest power of p which divides the order of N. Thus N possesses one or more Sylow groups of order p^m. We have in fact found two such subgroups of N, namely A and $P_\lambda^{-1}AP_\lambda$. On the other hand, A is invariant in N and, by the Corollary on p. 130, is therefore unique, i.e. we must have

$$P_\lambda^{-1}AP_\lambda = A.$$

Remembering that N was defined as the normalizer of A, we infer that
$$P_\lambda \subset N, \quad P_\lambda N = N,$$
whence
$$AP_\lambda N = AN = N.$$

However, this equation is impossible unless $\lambda = 1$. Hence all terms of (5.12) except the first are divisible by p, which at once leads to (5.13). This completes the proof of the theorem.

As an application we shall prove the following :

THEOREM 5. *Any group G whose order is of the form* pq, *where* p *and* q *are primes such that* $p \not\equiv 1$ *(mod.* q*) and* $q \not\equiv 1$ *(mod.* p*), is necessarily an Abelian group.*

Proof. The case in which $p = q$ having already been dealt with (Chapter IV, Theorem 5, p. 104), we shall assume that $(p, q) = 1$. Let $P(= \{P\})$ be a Sylow group of G corresponding to p. We know that the number of such subgroups is a divisor of pq and is of the form $1 + px$. Since $q \not\equiv 1$ (mod. p), it is necessarily equal to 1, the other factors of pq, namely p, q and pq, being incompatible with the conditions. Thus by the Corollary on p. 130 P is an invariant subgroup G of order p. Similarly $Q(= \{Q\})$ is an invariant subgroup of order q. Hence we have

$$PQ = QP$$

(see equation (4.8)), and by the Product Theorem (p. 56) the product of these two complexes represents a group of order pq/d, where d is the order of (P, Q). Since $(p, q) = 1$, the two groups can have only the unit element in common, i.e. $d = 1$ and therefore

$$G = PQ.$$

Again, by Chapter IV, Theorem 7, p. 106, every element of P commutes with every element of Q ; in particular

$$PQ = QP.$$

Thus the pq elements of G can be written

$$P^\alpha Q^\beta \quad \text{or} \quad Q^\beta P^\alpha \quad (\alpha = 0, 1, \ldots, p-1 ; \quad \beta = 0, 1, \ldots, q-1),$$

which evidently defines an Abelian group.

41. Prime Power Groups. This is the name given to groups of order p^m, where p is a prime. All Sylow groups are of this type. Prime power groups possess a number of interesting properties, one of which we encountered in Chapter IV, Theorem 2, p. 99, where we saw that a group G of order p^m always contains at least one invariant element P of order p. We have then

$$X^{-1}PX = P,$$

where X is any element of G, and *the cyclic group*

$$P = \{P\}$$

is an invariant subgroup of order p. This result may be generalized as follows :

THEOREM 6. *A group of order* p^m *possesses at least one invariant subgroup of order* p^μ, *where* $0 < \mu < \mathrm{m}$.

Proof. The theorem is true when $m = 2$, since the group is in that case Abelian (Chapter IV, Theorem 5, p. 104), and any element of order p generates an invariant subgroup of order p. Thus we have a basis for induction. Let G be a group of order p^m $(m > 2)$. Let P be an invariant subgroup of G of order p. The quotient group G/P is of order p^{m-1}. We may therefore assume that G/P has an invariant subgroup of order $p^{\mu-1}$. Such a group can be written in the form

$$A/P,$$

where A is an invariant subgroup of G, which must evidently be of order p^μ. (Chapter IV, Theorem 10, p. 111.)

COROLLARY. *All prime power groups are soluble.*

For a group G of order p^m possesses an invariant subgroup A of order p^{m-1}, which in turn contains an invariant subgroup of order p^{m-2}, etc. Thus we can construct a composition series

$$G \succ A_1 \succ A_2 \succ \ldots \succ A_{m-1} \succ I,$$

in which all composition indices are equal to p.

Example 1. *There can be no simple group of order 200.*
For since $200 = 5^2 \times 8$, the group contains k Sylow groups of
order 25, where k is of the form $1 + 5x$ ($x = 0, 1, 2, \ldots$) and
a divisor of 200. Since $(k, 5) = 1$, we must have $k \mid 8$,
which is impossible unless $x = 0$, i.e. there is a unique
invariant Sylow group of order 25. Thus the group is not
simple.

Example 2. *There can be no simple group of order 30.*
For if there were such a group, none of its Sylow groups
would be unique. Hence it would have $1 + 5(=6)$ Sylow
groups of order 5 comprising $6 \times 4 (=24)$ elements of
order 5. Also there would be $1 + 3 \times 3(=10)$ Sylow groups
of order 3, and so the total number of elements would
exceed 30.

Examples

(1) Show that A_4 has one Sylow group of order 4 and four
Sylow groups of order 3.

(2) Prove that there is no simple group of order 56.

(3) If G be a group of order $p^2 q$, where p and q are primes
such that q is less than p and not a factor of $p^2 - 1$, prove that
G is Abelian.

(4) Prove that any subgroup whose order is a power of p
(a prime factor of g) is contained in at least one of the Sylow
groups corresponding to p.

(5) Show that an invariant subgroup whose order is a
power of p is contained in every Sylow group corresponding to p.

(6) If every Sylow group of G is an invariant subgroup,
show that G is the direct product of its Sylow groups.

HINTS and ANSWERS. 2. Otherwise there would be eight
Sylow groups of order 7 and seven of order 8. 3. Prove that both
Sylow groups are unique and use Chapter IV, Theorem 7, p. 106.
4. Use Frobenius' expansion (Chapter II, Theorem 8, p. 60)
and apply it to the subgroup in question and a Sylow group.
6. Use Chapter IV, Theorem 7, p. 106.

CHAPTER VI

ABELIAN GROUPS

42. Introduction. It is evident that the theory of groups would be very much simpler if multiplication were commutative as well as associative. In fact our knowledge of Abelian groups is more complete and more systematic than that of any other class of groups, the most important feature being that we possess methods which make a survey of all abstract Abelian groups possible, a goal that is still quite remote in the case of non-commutative groups.

Throughout this chapter it will be assumed that the multiplication of all group elements is commutative, i.e.

$$AB = BA,$$

whence by (1.7), p. 5.

$$(AB)^m = A^m B^m. \qquad \cdots \qquad (6.1)$$

Again, every subgroup is an invariant subgroup, and the product

$$A_1 A_2 \ldots A_r \qquad \cdots \qquad (6.2)$$

of several subgroups A_i ($i = 1, 2, \ldots, r$) is itself a subgroup (Multiplication Theorem, p. 56). If no two of the groups A_i have an element other than I in common, the product (6.2) may be written as the *direct product*

$$A_1 \times A_2 \times \ldots \times A_r \qquad \cdots \qquad (6.3)$$

(see p. 46).

43. Sylow Groups of an Abelian Group. Since all subgroups of an Abelian group G are invariant, there is exactly one Sylow group corresponding to each prime that divides the order g of G (Corollary, p. 130). In fact, if

$$g = p_1^{\alpha_1} p_2^{\alpha_2} \ldots p_r^{\alpha_r}, \quad (p_i \neq p_j, \text{ if } i \neq j) \qquad . \quad (6.4)$$

then G has the r Sylow groups

$$A_1, A_2, \ldots, A_r$$

of orders

$$p^{\alpha_1}, p^{\alpha_2}, \ldots, p^{\alpha_r} \qquad . \qquad . \qquad . \quad (6.5)$$

respectively. Since the numbers (6.5) are relatively prime, it is clear that no two Sylow groups have an element other than I in common. Hence the group

$$A_1 \times A_2 \times \ldots \times A_r$$

is of order $p_1^{\alpha_1} p_2^{\alpha_2} \ldots, p_r^{\alpha_r}$ and is therefore identical with G. Thus   *This should be product, not sequence*

$$G = A_1 \times A_2 \times \ldots \times A_r, \qquad . \qquad . \quad (6.6)$$

and we have therefore come to the following conclusion:

THEOREM 1. *Every Abelian group is the direct product of its Sylow groups.*

In the case of Abelian groups the existence of *Sylow* groups may be established from first principles without the rather elaborate theory which was the subject of the preceding chapter.

Let p be one of the prime factors of the order g of G, and let A be the corresponding Sylow group of order p^α. This group has the following characteristic property:

THEOREM 2. *In an Abelian group the Sylow group of order p^α consists of all elements of G whose order is a power of p.*

Proof. Let R be the complex of those elements of G whose order is a power of p. If X and Y be any two such elements, we have by (6.1)

$$(XY)^f = X^f Y^f.$$

By taking for f a sufficiently high power of p, we can make each factor on the right-hand side equal to I, and hence

K

also the product on the left.   This proves that the complex
R is a group.

Evidently, since the order of any element of the Sylow
group A is a power of p,

$$A \subset R. \qquad . \qquad . \qquad . \qquad . \qquad (6.7)$$

On the other hand, we shall now prove that the opposite
relation is also true.   For suppose R were an element of
R not contained in A.   The product

$$A\{R\}$$

would then be a group more comprehensive than A and of
an order which, like those of A and $\{R\}$, is a power of p.
This would be a contradiction to the fact that A is a Sylow
group corresponding to p, i.e. one whose order is the greatest
possible power of p.   Hence we must have

$$R \subset A,$$

and in view of (6.7)

$$R = A,$$

which proves the theorem.

44. Basis of Abelian Groups.   The simplest Abelian
groups are the cyclic groups

$$C_m = \{A\}, \quad A^m = I.$$

We shall eventually arrive at the result that all Abelian
groups can be written as *direct products* of cyclic groups,
and we would meanwhile remind the reader of the few
instances of this theorem which we encountered in Chapter
II, § 16.

Let us first of all consider a group which is in fact
defined as a direct product of cyclic groups, thus

$$G = \{A_1\} \times \{A_2\} \times \ldots \times \{A_k\}, \qquad . \qquad . \qquad (6.8)$$

where A_i is of order m_i.   This is an Abelian group, and a
typical element of G may be written

$$G = A_1{}^{x_1} A_2{}^{x_2} \ldots A_k{}^{x_k} \quad (0 \leqslant x_i < m_i). \qquad . \qquad (6.9)$$

Since the factors of a direct product are independent (p. 46), this expression for G is unique. This is equivalent to saying that a relation of the form

$$A_1{}^{e_1}A_2{}^{e_2}\ldots A_k{}^{e_k}=I \qquad . \qquad . \qquad . \quad (6.10)$$

necessarily implies that

$$e_i \equiv 0 \;(\text{mod. } m_i) \quad (i=1,\,2,\,\ldots,\,k).$$

For a supposed equation

$$A_1{}^{x_1}A_2{}^{x_2}\ldots A_k{}^{x_k}=G=A_1{}^{y_1}A_2{}^{y_2}\ldots A_k{}^{y_k}$$

would at once lead to (6.10), where $e_i = x_i - y_i$. On comparing the number of elements on both sides of (6.8) we get

$$g=m_1m_2\ldots m_k. \qquad . \qquad . \qquad . \quad (6.11)$$

DEFINITION 1. *If in an Abelian group* G *there are elements* $A_1, A_2, \ldots, A_k$ *of orders* $m_1, m_2, \ldots, m_k$ *respectively such that every element* G *of* G *can be represented in the form*

$$G=A_1{}^{x_1}A_2{}^{x_2}\ldots A_k{}^{x_k} \quad \begin{pmatrix} 0 \leqslant x_i < m_i \\ i=1,\,2,\,\ldots,\,k \end{pmatrix} \quad . \quad (6.12)$$

in one, and only one, way, then $A_1, A_2, \ldots, A_k$ *are said to form a* **basis** *of* G.

Note that the uniqueness of the representation implies that the basis elements are independent.

Comparing (6.12) with (6.9) we see that *an Abelian group possesses a basis if, and only if, it can be written as a direct product of cyclic groups,* as in (6.8).

The set of basis elements (if it exists) is by no means completely determined by the group. This is indeed evident even in the case of a single cyclic factor. For if C be of order m, then

$$\{C\} = \{C^t\},$$

where t is any integer prime to m.

Again, let

$$m = rs, \quad \text{where } (r,\,s) = 1.$$

The group $\{C\}$ of order m contains the subgroups

$$\{C^s\} \quad \text{and} \quad \{C^r\}$$

of orders r and s respectively. Since $(r, s) = 1$, these two groups can have no element in common except I. Hence $\{C^s\}\{C^r\}$, which may also be written as a direct product, comprises all $rs(=m)$ elements of $\{C\}$, thus

$$\{C\} = \{C^s\} \times \{C^r\}. \qquad . \qquad . \qquad (6.13)$$

Conversely, consider a direct product

$$\{A\} \times \{B\},$$

whose factors are of orders r and s respectively, where $(r, s) = 1$. The element

$$C = AB$$

is of order rs. For we have $C^{rs} = A^{rs}B^{rs} = I$. On the other hand, if m were an integer such that $C^m = A^m B^m = I$, it would follow that $A^m = B^{-m}$. But I is the only element which belongs both to $\{A\}$ and $\{B\}$. Hence $A^m = I = B^{-m}$, i.e. m must be a multiple of r and s, and hence also of rs, which means that AB is of order rs, thus

$$\{AB\} = \{A\} \times \{B\}. \qquad . \qquad . \qquad (6.14)$$

We can summarize (6.13) and (6.14) in the statement

$$C_{rs} = C_r \times C_s, \; if \; (r, s) = 1. \qquad . \qquad . \qquad (6.15)$$

It follows in particular that by a repeated application of (6.15) we can always arrange that the orders of the cyclic groups in (6.8) are *powers of primes*. In fact, if

$$m = p^\alpha q^\beta r^\gamma \ldots$$

we have

$$C_m = C_{p^\alpha} \times C_{q^\beta} \times C_{r^\gamma} \times \ldots . \qquad . \qquad . \qquad (6.16)$$

45. The Fundamental Theorem.

THEOREM 3.* *Every Abelian group is the direct product of cyclic groups whose orders are powers of primes.*

* G. A. Miller suggests that this theorem be regarded as the fourth in order of importance, being preceded only by the theorems of Lagrange (p. 34), Sylow (p. 127) and Cayley (p. 80), see G. A. Miller, H. F. Blichfeldt and L. E. Dickson, *Theory and Application of Finite Groups* (New York, 1916).

Proof.   (i) Let **G** be an Abelian group of order g where

$$g = p_1^{\alpha_1} p_2^{\alpha_2} \ldots p_i^{\alpha_l}.$$

We have seen that every Abelian group is the direct product of its Sylow groups (Theorem 1, p. 137), thus

$$\mathbf{G} = \mathbf{A}_1 \times \mathbf{A}_2 \times \ldots \times \mathbf{A}_l,$$

where the factors on the right-hand side correspond to the different primes dividing the order of **G**. It is therefore sufficient to prove the theorem for an Abelian group whose order, like that of a Sylow group, is a power of a prime. The orders of the cyclic groups which appear as factors in the direct product will then automatically be powers of primes.

(ii) Let **A** be an Abelian group of order p^m. We wish to show that there exists a set of independent elements such that every element X of **A** may be represented as

$$X = A_1^{x_1} A_2^{x_2} \ldots A_k^{x_k}.$$

The theorem is evidently true when $m = 1$. For **A** is then necessarily cyclic. We may therefore proceed by induction and assume that the theorem holds for all Abelian groups of order p^μ, where μ is less than m.

Let A_1 be an element of maximum order. If A_1 is of order p^m, then

$$\mathbf{A} = \{A_1\}$$

and there is nothing further to prove. Suppose then that the order of A_1 is p^{m_1}, where $m_1 < m$. The order of any element of **A** is of the form p^f, where

$$f \leqslant m_1 < m. \quad . \quad . \quad . \quad (6.17)$$

We note that $X^{p^{m_1}} = I$ for every element of **A**.

(iii) Consider the cyclic subgroup

$$\mathbf{A}_1 = \{A_1\}.$$

The quotient group $\mathbf{A}/\mathbf{A}_1$ is of order p^{m-m_1}. It consists of all complexes $A_1 X$ and by hypothesis may be derived from a set of basis elements

$$A_1 B_2, A_1 B_3, \ldots, A_1 B_k, \qquad \qquad (6.18)$$

whose orders will be denoted by

$$p^{m_2}, p^{m_3}, \ldots, p^{m_k} \qquad \qquad (6.19)$$

respectively, where

$$m_2 \geqslant m_3 \geqslant \ldots \geqslant m_k. \qquad \qquad (6.20)$$

Since A_1 is the unit element of A/A_1, this means that

$$(A_1 B_i)^{p^{m_i}} = A_1 B_i^{p^{m_i}} = A_1 \quad (i = 2, 3, \ldots, k),$$

i.e. p^{m_i} is the exponent of the least positive power of B_i that lies in A_1. Hence we may put

$$B_i^{p^{m_i}} = A_1^{t_i}. \qquad \qquad (6.21)$$

It follows that p^{m_i} cannot exceed the order p^{f_i} of B_i and, in view of (6.17), is certainly not greater than p^{m_1}. Hence we have $m_i \leqslant f_i \leqslant m_1$ $(i = 2, 3, \ldots, k)$, and on using (6.20),

$$m_1 \geqslant m_2 \geqslant \ldots \geqslant m_k. \qquad \qquad (6.22)$$

Raising (6.21) to the $(p^{m_1 - m_i})$th power, we get

$$B_i^{p^{m_1}} = I = A_1^{p^{m_1}(t_i/p^{m_i})}.$$

Since A_1 is of order p^{m_1}, it follows that t_i/p^{m_i} is an integer u_i, so that we may write

$$t_i = u_i p^{m_i}.$$

Thus if we put

$$A_i = A_1^{-u_i} B_i \quad (i = 2, 3, \ldots, k), \qquad (6.23)$$

we have

$$A_i^{p^{m_i}} = A_1^{-t_i} B_i^{p^{m_i}} = I \quad (i \geqslant 2), \qquad (6.24)$$

by (6.21). Since

$$A_1 A_i = (A_1 A_1^{-u_i}) B_i = A_1 B_i,$$

the basis (6.18) may be written in the alternative form

$$A_1 A_2, A_1 A_3, \ldots, A_1 A_k, \quad . \quad . \quad . \quad (6.25)$$

and we note that, according to (6.24), A_i is of order p^{m_i}.

(iv) Starting from the basis (6.25) of A/A_1, we shall deduce that the elements

$$A_1, A_2, \ldots, A_k \quad . \quad . \quad . \quad (6.26)$$

form a basis of A. Indeed, if X be any element of A, the complex AX is an element of A/A_1 and can therefore be expressed in terms of (6.25), thus

$$A_1 X = (A_1 A_2)^{x_2} (A_1 A_3)^{x_3} \ldots (A_1 A_k)^{x_k},$$

i.e.

$$A_1 X = A_1 A_2{}^{x_2} A_3{}^{x_3} \ldots A_k{}^{x_k}.$$

It follows that

$$X (A_2{}^{x_2} A_3{}^{x_k} \ldots A_k{}^{x_k})^{-1}$$

is an element of A_1, say $A_1{}^{x_1}$. Hence

$$X = A_1{}^{x_1} A_2{}^{x_2} \ldots A_k{}^{x_k}.$$

It remains to show that the elements (6.26) are independent. Suppose we had a relation

$$A_1{}^{e_1} A_2{}^{e_2} \ldots A_k{}^{e_k} = I. \quad . \quad . \quad . \quad (6.27)$$

Premultiplying by A_1 we should find that

$$(A_1 A_2)^{e_2} (A_1 A_3)^{e_3} \ldots (A_1 A_k)^{e_k} = A_1.$$

Since the complexes (6.25) are by hypothesis independent, we infer that e_i $(i \geqslant 2)$ is a multiple of the order of $A_1 A_i$ (when regarded as an element of A/A_1), thus

$$e_i = z_i p^{m_i} \quad (i \geqslant 2). \quad . \quad . \quad . \quad (6.28)$$

Substituting in (6.27) and using (6.24), we obtain

$$A_1{}^{e_1} = I,$$

whence finally

$$e_1 = z_1 p^{m_1}.$$

Hence an equation of the type (6.27) is impossible unless

each factor is separately equal to the unit element. This completes the proof of the theorem.

COROLLARY. *In every Abelian group the order of any element is a factor of the maximal order; i.e. there exists an element of order* h *such that every element of the group is a solution of* $X^h = I$.

Proof. The proposition has already been established for Abelian groups whose order is a power of a prime (see (6.17)). In the general case let G be written as the direct product of its Sylow groups, thus

$$G = A_1 \times A_2 \times \ldots \times A_l. \qquad . \qquad . \qquad (6.29)$$

If M_λ be an element of maximal order μ_λ in A_λ, we know that every element X_λ of A_l satisfies the equation $X^{\mu_\lambda} = I$. Hence it follows that

$$M = M_1 M_2 \ldots M_l$$

is an element of order μ, where

$$\mu = \mu_1 \mu_2 \ldots \mu_l.$$

On the other hand, every element

$$X = X_1 X_2 \ldots X_l$$

of G satisfies the equation $X^\mu = I$.

46. The Elementary Divisors and Invariants of an Abelian Group. It appears that there is considerable latitude in choosing the basis elements of a given Abelian group. But while the basis elements themselves are not uniquely determined, it will be shown that their orders possess invariant properties which completely specify the structure of the group. We have already seen that the orders of the basis elements are powers of primes if the basis is constructed in accordance with Theorem 3.

THEOREM 4. *If the orders of the basis elements are powers of primes, they are called the* **elementary divisors** *of the Abelian group. They are completely determined by the group itself and, apart from their sequence, do not depend on the particular basis chosen.*

Proof. (i) It is sufficient to prove the theorem for a group whose order is a power of a prime, since the elementary divisors of any Abelian group are those of its Sylow groups taken together.

(ii) Let G be an Abelian group of order p^m and suppose that we have two sets of basis elements :

$$A_1, A_2, \ldots, A_k \qquad . \qquad . \qquad . \ (6.30)$$

of orders

$$p^{m_1}, p^{m_2}, \ldots, p^{m_k}$$

respectively and

$$B_1, B_2, \ldots, B_t . \qquad . \qquad . \qquad . \ (6.31)$$

of orders

$$p^{n_1}, p^{n_2}, \ldots, p^{n_t}$$

respectively. In order to simplify the notation let us put

$$\mu_i = p^{m_i} \ (i = 1, 2, \ldots, k) ; \quad \nu_j = p^{n_j} \ (j = 1, 2, \ldots, t). \ (6.32)$$

The basis elements may be arranged in such a way that

$$\mu_1 \geqslant \mu_2 \geqslant \ldots \geqslant \mu_k (>1) . \qquad . \qquad . \ (6.33)$$

and

$$\nu_1 \geqslant \nu_2 \geqslant \ldots \geqslant \nu_t (>1). . \qquad . \qquad . \ (6.34)$$

We have of course

$$p^m = \mu_1 \mu_2 \ldots \mu_k = \nu_1 \nu_2 \ldots \nu_t$$

(see (6.11), p. 139). It is required to show that $k = t$ and $\mu_i = \nu_i \ (i = 1, 2, \ldots, k)$.

Suppose the theorem were false and let μ_f be the first number in the set (6.33) to differ from the corresponding number in (6.34) ; thus we have

$$\nu_1 = \mu_1, \ \nu_2 = \mu_2, \ \ldots, \ \nu_{f-1} = \mu_{f-1}, \qquad . \qquad . \ (6.35)$$

but $\nu_f \neq \mu_f$. To fix the ideas let

$$\nu_f > \mu_f. \qquad . \qquad . \qquad . \qquad . \ (6.36)$$

(If $f = 1$, equations (6.35) are to be omitted.)

(iii) In every Abelian group G the totality of elements which can be represented as the μ_fth power of some other element, forms a subgroup H, say ; for if

$$X = U^{\mu_f}, \quad Y = V^{\mu_f},$$

we have

$$XY = (UV)^{\mu_f}.$$

The definition of H is independent of any basis of G. On the other hand, a basis of H may be constructed simply by raising all basis elements of G to the μ_fth power. Any element whose order is a factor of μ_f is thereby reduced to the unit element and should be omitted. Generally, an element of order μ_i is changed into one of order μ_i/μ_f. Since by (6.32) we have $\mu_i \mid \mu_f$ if, and only if, $\mu_i \leqslant \mu_f$, it follows that the elements

$$A_1{}^{\mu_f}, A_2{}^{\mu_f}, \ldots, A_{f-1}{}^{\mu_f}$$

form a basis of H. They are independent and of orders

$$\mu_1/\mu_f, \mu_2/\mu_f, \ldots, \mu_{f-1}/\mu_f$$

respectively, whence the order of H is found to be given by

$$h = (\mu_1\mu_2 \ldots \mu_{f-1})/\mu_f{}^{f-1}. \qquad . \qquad . \quad (6.37)$$

It is equally true that the μ_fth powers of the elements (6.31) would also provide a basis of H provided we retain only those amongst them whose orders were originally greater than μ_f. Although we cannot tell exactly which elements of (6.31) are thus involved, it is clear from (6.34) and (6.36) that

$$B_1{}^{\mu_f}, B_2{}^{\mu_f}, \ldots, B_f{}^{\mu_f}$$

are certainly to be included in such a basis of H. These elements are of orders

$$\nu_1/\mu_f, \nu_2/\mu_f, \ldots, \nu_f/\mu_f$$

respectively. Thus it would follow that

$$h \geqslant (\nu_1\nu_2 \ldots \nu_{f-1}\nu_f)/\mu_f{}^f.$$

Substituting for h from (6.37), we obtain

$$(\mu_1\mu_2\ldots\mu_{f-1})/\mu_f^{\,f-1} \geqslant (\nu_1\nu_2\ldots\nu_f)/\mu_f^{\,f},$$

whence by (6.35)

$$1 \geqslant \nu_f/\mu_f,$$

in contradiction to (6.36). Thus we must conclude that the sets (6.33) and (6.34) are, in fact, identical.

DEFINITION 2. *An Abelian group of order* p^m *is said to be of* **type** $(\mathrm{m}_1, \mathrm{m}_2, \ldots, \mathrm{m}_k)$ *if it is the direct product of cyclic groups of orders*

$$p^{m_1}, p^{m_2}, \ldots, p^{m_k}, \qquad \cdot \qquad \cdot \qquad (6.37)$$

where

$$\bar{m}_1 \geqslant m_2 \geqslant \ldots \geqslant m_k > 0, \quad m_1 + m_2 + \ldots + m_k = m, \quad (6.38)$$

i.e. if (6.37) *are the elementary divisors of the group.*

Thus there are as many different Abelian groups of order p^m as there are *partitions* of m satisfying (6.38).

E.g., there are three Abelian groups of order 8 ($= 2^3$) corresponding to the types (3), (2, 1), (1, 1, 1) (see Chapter II, p. 51) respectively.

Suppose next that the order g of an Abelian group G involves more than one prime, say

$$g = p^a q^b r^c, \ldots$$

so that G has Sylow groups of orders $p^a, q^b, r^c, \ldots$ respectively. The elementary divisors of G may be arranged in an array * thus

$$\left.\begin{array}{l} p^{a_1} \ p^{a_2}, \ \ldots \ (a_1 \geqslant a_2 \geqslant \ldots, a_1 + a_2 + \ldots = a) \\ q^{b_1}, \ q^{b_2}, \ \ldots \ (b_1 \geqslant b_2 \geqslant \ldots, b_1 + b_2 + \ldots = b) \\ r^{c_1}, \ r^{c_2}, \ \ldots \ (c_1 \geqslant c_2 \geqslant \ldots, c_1 + c_2 + \ldots = c) \\ \cdots\cdots\cdots \qquad \cdots \qquad\qquad \cdots \end{array}\right\}. \quad (6.39)$$

Each row contains the elementary divisors of a Sylow group, and G is the direct product of all the cyclic groups

* Such an array is not, in general, rectangular. But, if desired, empty spaces may be filled up with units in order to make the rows equally long.

whose orders are listed in (6.39). It is impossible to carry the decomposition of G into cyclic groups any further, and in that respect the elementary divisors of an Abelian group correspond to its ultimate constituents.

On the other hand, if we waive the condition that the orders of the cyclic factors should be powers of primes, several of the cyclic groups whose orders are prime to one another may be combined into one. Thus by applying (6.16) we can gather the cyclic groups whose orders are given in the first column of (6.39) into a single cyclic group

$$C_{n_1} = C_{p}{}^{a_1} \times C_{q}{}^{b_1} \times C_{r}{}^{c_1} \times \ldots.$$

Similarly, corresponding to the second column of (6.39), we get

$$C_{n_2} = C_{p}{}^{a_2} \times C_{q}{}^{b_2} \times C_{r}{}^{c_2} \times \ldots$$

etc. Since $a_1 \geqslant a_2$, $b_1 \geqslant b_2$, $c_1 \geqslant c_2$, $\ldots$ we have $n_2 \mid n_1$, and generally

$$n_i \mid n_{i-1}.$$

DEFINITION 3. *The numbers* n_1, n_2, $\ldots$ *obtained by multiplying the numbers in each column of the array of elementary divisors are called the* **invariants** * *of the group* G. *They are characterized by the following properties*

(i) $\qquad G = C_{n_1} \times C_{n_2} \times \ldots \quad (g = n_1 n_2 \ldots)$

(ii) $\qquad n_i \mid n_{i-1} \quad (i = 2, 3, \ldots).$

The invariants are *uniquely* determined by the elementary divisors and, conversely, if we resolve each invariant into prime factors, we recover the array of elementary divisors. Thus the invariants are completely specified by the group itself and do not depend on the choice of basis.

When the order of the group is the power of a prime, the elementary divisors are the same as the invariants. But when the order is divisible by at least two primes, the number of invariants is less than that of the elementary divisors.

* The nomenclature is not completely standardized, some authors using the term 'invariants' for what we have called elementary divisors, or indiscriminately for both concepts.

Example 1. *An Abelian group of order* p^m *and type* $(m_1, m_2, \ldots, m_k)$ *contains* $p^k - 1$ *elements of order* p. For let $A_1, A_2, \ldots, A_k$ be a basis of the group and consider the equation $X^p = I$. If

$$X = A_1^{x_1} A_2^{x_2} \ldots A_k^{x_k} \qquad . \qquad . \qquad . \quad (6.40)$$

be a solution, we have

$$I = A_1^{px_1} A_2^{px_2} \ldots A_k^{px_k},$$

whence on account of the independence of the basis elements

$$px_i \equiv 0 \pmod{p^{m_i}},$$

i.e.

$$x_i \equiv 0 \pmod{p^{m_i-1}} \quad (i = 1, 2, \ldots, k).$$

For a fixed value of i there are p solutions compatible with the conditions $0 \leqslant x_i < p^{m_i}$, namely $x_i = \lambda p^{m_i-1}$, where $\lambda = 0, 1, 2, \ldots, p - 1$. Substituting in (6.40), we see that the equation $X^p = I$ is satisfied by p^k distinct elements, including the unit element. Thus the group contains exactly $p^k - 1$ elements of order p.

Example 2. *Find the Sylow groups, elementary divisors and invariants of the group*

$$A^{30} = B^{12} = I, \quad AB = BA.$$

The order of this group is $360 (= 2^3 \times 3^2 \times 5)$. Its Sylow groups are of orders 8, 9, 5 respectively, and may be specified as follows :

$\{B^3, A^{15}\}$ of order 8 and elementary divisors $(4, 2)$,
$\{A^{10}, B^4\}$ of order 9 and elementary divisors $(3, 3)$,
$\{A^6\}$ of order 5 and elementary divisor (5).

The invariants are accordingly

$$n_1 = 4 \times 3 \times 5 = 60, \quad n_2 = 2 \times 3 = 6.$$

Examples

(1) Prove that if the order of an Abelian group is not divisible by a square, it must be cyclic.

(2) Show that the greatest invariant (n_1) may be characterized as the maximum order, or alternatively as the L.C.M. of all orders in the group.

(3) Show that the remainder classes prime to 24 form an Abelian group of order 8 $(= \phi(24))$ and type $(1, 1, 1)$.

(4) Find the Sylow groups, elementary divisors and invariants of the following Abelian groups : (i) $A^{15} = B^4 = I$, (ii) $A^{20} = B^6 = C^5 = I$, (iii) $A^{12} = I$, $A^6 = B^{15}$.

(5) By comparing the number of generating elements on both sides of (6.16), deduce the well-known formula

$$\phi(m) = m\left(1 - \frac{1}{p}\right)\left(1 - \frac{1}{q}\right). \ldots$$

(6) Show that an Abelian group of order g has at least one subgroup whose order is equal to any pre-assigned factor of g.

(7) Prove that every Abelian group is soluble.

(8) Prove that in an Abelian group of order p^3 and type $(1, 1, 1)$ a basis may be chosen in $p^3(p^3 - 1)(p^2 - 1)(p - 1)$ ways. Generalize this result.

(9) Show that an Abelian group of order p^{2u+v} and type $(2, 2, \ldots, 2, 1, 1, \ldots, 1)(u$ 2's and v 1's) contains p^{u+v-1} $(p^u - 1)/(p - 1)$ cyclic subgroups of order p^2 and $(p^{u+v} - 1)$ $(p^{u+v-1} - 1)/(p^2 - 1)(p - 1)$ non-cyclic subgroups of order p^2.

HINTS and ANSWERS. 3. No element is of order greater than 2. 4. (i) $\{B\}$, $\{A^5\}$, $\{A^3\}$; (4), (3), (5), 60. (ii) $\{A^5, B^3\}$, $\{B^2\}$, $\{A^4, C\}$; (4, 2), (3), (5, 5); 60, 10. (iii) $\{A^3\}$, $\{A^4, B^{10}\}$, $\{B^6\}$; (4), (3, 3), (5); 60, 3. 5. A cyclic group of order n has $\phi(n)$ generating elements ; use (1.28). 6. Establish the result first for cases in which $g = p^m$. 8. There are $p^3 - 1$ elements of order p (see Example 1, p. 149), any one of which may be taken as the first basis element. The cyclic group generated by the first basis element contains $p - 1$ elements of order p so that only $(p^3 - 1) - (p - 1) = p^2 - p$ are left from which the second basis element can be selected, etc. 9. (i) There are $p^{2u+v} - p^{u+v}$ elements of order p^2 and a fixed cyclic group of order p^2 has $p^2 - p$ generating elements ; (ii) two independent elements of order p can be chosen in $(p^{u+v} - 1)(p^{u+v} - p)$ ways. A fixed group of type $(1, 1)$ has $(p^2 - 1)(p^2 - p)$ alternative sets of generators.

BIBLIOGRAPHY

BURNSIDE, WM., *Theory of groups of finite order*, 2nd ed., 1911.

CARMICHAEL, R. D., *Introduction to the theory of groups of finite order*, 1937.

HILTON, H., *An Introduction to the theory of groups of finite order*, 1908.

MATHEWSON, L. C., *Elementary theory of groups*, 1930.

MILLER, G. A., BLICHFELD, H. F., DICKSON, L. E., *Theory and applications of finite groups*, 1916.

SPEISER, A., *Theorie der Gruppen von endlicher Ordnung*, 2nd ed., 1927.

INDEX

The numbers refer to the pages